4.95

D1083411

NO LONGER PROPERTY OF
BRESCIA COLLEGE LIBRARY

THE SUN AND STARS

the physics and astronomy of

JOHN C. BRANDT

Kitt Peak National Observatory

✳

✳

✳

the sun and stars

McGraw-Hill Book Company

New York · St. Louis · San Francisco · Toronto · London · Sydney

BRESCIA COLLEGE LIBRARY
OWENSBORO, KENTUCKY

McGraw-Hill Series in
UNDERGRADUATE ASTRONOMY
Gerald S. Hawkins, Consulting Editor

BALDWIN: the moon
BRANDT: the sun and stars
HAWKINS: meteors, comets, and meteorites
HODGE: galaxies and cosmology
LUNDQUIST: space science

523.013
B821

the sun and stars

Copyright © 1966 by McGraw-Hill, Inc. All Rights Reserved.
Printed in the United States of America. This book, or
parts thereof, may not be reproduced in any form without
permission of the publishers.

Library of Congress Catalog Card Number 66–20715

1 2 3 4 5 6 7 8 9 0 BN 7 3 2 1 0 6 9 8 7 6

TO KARL AND KEITH

TWO INDOMITABLE SPIRITS

31940

PREFACE

This book forms part of a series covering the broad area of astronomy, astrophysics, and space science. Each book attempts to fulfill a need of an undergraduate student studying astronomy, physics, or space science. Although written primarily for the undergraduate student majoring in the physical sciences, the present work should also provide a useful reference for more advanced students who wish to augment their knowledge in this field.

It has been necessary to divide the subject matter into rather broad areas of interest in order to cover all topics in a few relatively short monographs. This book deals with the stars—their properties, structure, and evolution. The emphasis throughout is on understanding the physical situations important in the physics of stars. Thus some traditional astronomical subjects may not receive mention or full development. In view of the immense subject implied by the title, this restriction is necessary to keep the size of this monograph manageable and to preserve continuity.

The Sun is the only star subject to detailed scrutiny, and hence several chapters are devoted wholly or partially to solar physics. The concepts developed for the solar case are then extended to other stars. The comparatively recent fields of stellar evolution and stellar populations are given strong emphasis, since these concepts have contributed strongly to the understanding of a bewildering array of seemingly unrelated facts concerning stars. Variable stars are included as a means of studying the problems mentioned in other chapters and not as a subject in themselves.

Bibliographical notes have been included as an aid to independent reading and deepening understanding of the material.

Review questions and problems relating to the text have been included in a separate section. These form a basic tool for assessing the study program if the book is used as a college text. For a more advanced reader, the questions show the type of problem that might readily come to mind as he goes through the text. The interested layman or nonscientist can ignore the problems if he wishes.

John C. Brandt

CONTENTS

THE SUN AND STARS

※ 1 ※ **introduction**

Mankind has long and for good reason engaged in the worship of the Sun. Its great importance in providing heat and light has accorded the Sun a dominant place in the life and religions of peoples, such as the Aztecs, Mayas, and Incas, through the ages; astronomy and astrophysics find themselves in a similar situation because of our proximity to the Sun. It is an only slightly mixed blessing.

In terms of physical parameters (such as mass, temperature, abundances of the elements) and in terms of parameters related to galactic structure (such as space velocity, location in the galaxy), the Sun should be considered a normal star—one of some 10^{11} stars which make up our galaxy, the Milky Way galaxy. This last statement more than justifies its occupying the attention of approximately one-half of this treatise. However, the general "normality" of the Sun must be qualified in one extremely important respect; the Sun is a single star, i.e., not a member of a binary or multiple system. Various methods of estimating the number of binaries roughly agree in asserting that *approximately two-thirds of the stars in the galaxy are members of binary or multiple systems.* Hence, we must constantly guard against generalizations from our solar experience which are too sweeping. On the other hand, we have no evidence that this problem is extremely important for the structure and evolution of the stars, except in the case of fairly close systems (see Chapter 7).

Our proximity to the Sun enables us to gain a number of facts which we take for granted for the Sun but which are very difficult to obtain for other stars. The study of planetary and asteroidal motions gives (from Kepler's third law—see Chapter 5) the mass of the Sun ($M_\odot = 1.99 \times 10^{33}$ g) to a precision which far exceeds that obtainable for any other star. The planetary studies also give an accurate mean distance of the Sun from the Earth—the astronomical unit (AU), which equals 1.496×10^{13} cm. This number and the mean angular diameter of $31' 59''$ immediately give the value of the solar radius, $R_\odot = 6.96 \times 10^{10}$ cm. Studies of the total solar radiation can be combined with the geometrical values to give the total solar luminosity, $L_\odot = 3.9 \times 10^{33}$ ergs/sec. The solar effective temperature, the temperature of a blackbody the size of the Sun required to produce the solar luminosity, can be computed from the Stefan-Boltzmann law,

$$L_\odot = 4\pi\, R_\odot^2\, \sigma T_{eff}{}^4 \qquad (1.1)$$

Here $\sigma = 5.7 \times 10^{-5}$ erg/(cm^2) (sec) (deg)^4, and this quantity is the Stefan-Boltzmann constant. One finds $T_{eff} = 5750°$K for the Sun. It should be emphasized that these accurate numbers are made possible because we know the linear scale of the solar system with precision.

Our ability to resolve the solar disk enables us to determine the rate of the solar rotation and the equatorial acceleration (i.e., the fact that the Sun rotates faster at the equator than near the poles) and to study such disk phenomena as the granulation (Chapter 2), limb darkening (Chapter 2), sunspots (Chapter 3), and flares (Chapter 3). These latter phenomena will not be discussed further here, but it is clear that the possibility of their study leads to a depth of knowledge and understanding of the atmosphere of the Sun which is impossible for other stars.

If a quantity is ejected isotropically from a star, the flux of this quantity (be it particles or photons) generally decreases as the inverse square of the distance from the star. Since the nearest star is some 3×10^5 AU distant, the inverse square reduction for the *nearest* star is already $\sim 10^{-11}$ when compared with the radiation or particles from the Sun. Hence, it is not hard to understand why the Sun is the only individual star from which radio waves have been detected and why certain extreme ultraviolet and x-ray emissions have been detected only from the Sun. (Here, we take the extreme ultraviolet to extend from 100 to 1,000 Å and the x-ray region from 0.1 to 100 Å; the angstrom (Å) is 10^{-8} cm.) Similarly, the Sun is the only star for which we have direct and reasonably accurate measurements of an outflowing of matter; this matter, called the solar wind, has been measured by space probes sent far from the Earth.

The Earth is also fortunate enough to have a satellite, the Moon, whose angular size as viewed from the Earth is approximately the same as that of the Sun. This circumstance permits the study of the outer solar atmosphere with relative ease during eclipse, when the lower, brighter parts of the solar atmosphere are occulted by the Moon. Our knowledge of the chromosphere and corona has been greatly enhanced because of eclipse studies and provides a basis for speculation concerning the chromospheres and coronae of other stars; thus, the fact that the Earth has the Moon is an advantage to the study of stellar astronomy, an advantage not always appreciated as such by stellar (dark-time) astronomers.

We now describe the properties of the Sun with respect to the other stars in our galaxy; we deal here mostly with relative values since several absolute values are given just above in connection with our accurate knowledge of the scale of the solar system. In terms of luminosity, stars some 10^5 times brighter and 10^4 times fainter than the Sun are known. The temperature (specifically the temperature appropriate to the surface regions, called the effective temperature) of so-called normal stars ranges from 2000 to 30,000°K; the Sun is intermediately placed at about 6000°K (see Figure 5.1). The known masses of stars range from approximately 0.1 to 50 $M_\odot$ (see Figure 5.8); stellar radii vary from 0.1 to 200 $R_\odot$. In all cases, the Sun's value is intermediate; this fact is indeed one of great fortune for the study of stellar astronomy.

In the galaxy, the Sun is near the plane of the galaxy at a distance of approximately 10 kpc from the center or nucleus (1 kpc = kiloparsec = 3.1×10^{21} cm; see Chapter 5 for the definition of the parsec). It seems to be at an inner edge of a spiral arm and is a member of the galactic disk population, the stars of which constitute the flat, fast-rotating disk of the galaxy. The Sun has a rotation velocity about the galactic nucleus of some 250 km/sec, and a peculiar motion (measured relative to the stars in the solar neighborhood taken as a group) of about 20 km/sec directed toward a point in the constellation Hercules. Again the Sun seems to be completely typical.

Our general approach will be to exploit our knowledge of the Sun in the discussion of stellar phenomena as much as possible. We conclude this introductory chapter with a brief (historical) survey of the development of some of the ideas concerning the structure and evolution of the Sun and stars. Chapters 2 and 3 discuss the solar atmosphere and solar activity. Chapter 4 discusses the solar interior and concludes with the alterations required for the discussion of the various types of stars. Chapter 5 describes the methods of obtaining the basic data relevant to the stars (masses, radii, distances, temperatures, etc.) and the principal results, including the Hertzsprung-Russell diagram. This chapter concludes with a discussion of stellar atmospheres from the viewpoint of explaining the spectral sequence. Chapter 6 covers the modern theories of stellar evolution and the interpretation of the Hertzsprung-Russell diagram. Chapter 7 contains a survey of selected variable stars of astrophysical or evolutionary significance.

1.2 EARLY STUDIES OF THE SOLAR SURFACE

Modern studies of the surface of the Sun are generally taken to have begun with the telescopic observations of sunspots in 1611. Naked-eye sunspots are known back to circa 300 B.C. (attributed to Theophrastus of Athens), and numerous references are found in the Chinese, Japanese, and Korean annals. Little reference to naked-eye sunspots is found in the western literature; this fact may be due to the Aristotelian dictum stating that the Sun was a perfect body and, hence, one without blemish.

The discovery of telescopic sunspots in 1611 was made by four men independently: Fabricius, Galileo, Scheiner, and Harriot. It was immediately realized that spots occurred in groups and in restricted locations and that the Sun rotated with a period of about one month. Further knowledge concerning sunspots was to come quite slowly.

In 1769, it was noticed that the penumbrae of sunspots exhibited anomalous behavior as sunspots approached the limb of the Sun. The portion of the sunspot penumbra toward the limb remains essentially unchanged, but the part away from the limb decreases in size and disappears. This phenomenon is called the Wilson effect and is generally thought to show that sunspots are saucerlike depressions. Again, further knowledge was to come slowly.

The number of sunspots on the Sun is not constant but varies from relatively small (called sunspot minimum) to relatively large (called sunspot maximum). The general periodicity of the sunspot phenomenon was established in 1843 by Schwabe (while searching for the supposed but nonexistent intra-Mercurian planet, Vulcan), who determined a period of approximately 10 years between successive maxima or minima. Carrington discovered (circa 1860) the equatorial acceleration of the Sun from his sunspot observations and also established that the average latitude of sunspots decreases during the solar cycle (known as Spörer's law). Carrington shares with Hodgson the distinction of making the first observation of a solar flare on September 1, 1859. Wolf utilized all available observations of sunspots to establish the period of the solar cycle at 11 years; in 1848, he introduced the sunspot number R, which is still in use (see Section 3.3).

Studies of solar-disk phenomena besides sunspots properly began with Galileo's observations of bright areas near sunspots, called faculae (see Section 3.4). The solar granulation (shown in Figure 2.9) was observed visually by Carrington; these visual observations were confirmed photographically a few years later by Janssen. The granulation photographs taken by Janssen are remarkable and remained unequaled for decades. The solar limb darkening (discussed in Section 2.1) was studied by Secchi, who used daguerreotype images and a thermoelectric pile with the directly projected solar image; the latter method indicated that the brightness at the limb was about one-half the brightness at the disk center—in rough agreement with modern values.

Further progress in the study of the Sun outside of eclipse was made with the introduction of photographic and spectroscopic techniques; see Chapters 2 and 3 for a summary of modern developments, notably the discovery of strong magnetic fields in sunspots by G. E. Hale.

Observations of the Sun during solar eclipses led to the discovery of prominences and the corona; the latter at least must have been known from antiquity. The first problem which arises may strike us as amusing, namely, whether these "appendages" belong to the Sun or the Moon, since they are observed only at the time of solar eclipse. At the eclipses of 1851 and 1860, it was established that they were solar in origin by observing the Moon move over them. An independent confirmation came in 1868 when Janssen and Lockyer discovered that they could view solar prominences outside of eclipse by using a spectrometer to help reduce the scattered light. By 1931, even the corona could be observed outside of eclipse by means of the "coronagraph" of B. Lyot.

Spectroscopic studies of the Sun were begun visually in 1824 by Fraunhofer and continued by Huggins and Secchi. By comparison with laboratory spectra, the existence of many elements, known terrestrially, was established for the Sun. By 1890, Rowland could give a list of 36 elements whose existence on the Sun was regarded as certain. In 1895, helium was "added to the list." Its addition to the list depended on its terrestrial identification by Ramsey from mineral samples, for it had been observed on the Sun ever since its discovery in 1868 by Lockyer; helium thus derives its name from its method of discovery. This general process, namely, attributing unfamiliar lines to a new and unknown element, was repeated for the cases of "coronium" and "nebulium"; unfortunately, only helium was a new element. The others were simply familiar elements in unfamiliar stages of ionization.

The existence of the absorption (Fraunhofer) lines in the solar spectrum required explanation and led to the concept of the reversing layer. The photosphere was thought to emit a continuous spectrum; an overlying, cooler layer of gas would absorb at the characteristic wavelengths of the cooler gas. Thus, the solar spectrum would be deficient in light at the characteristic wavelengths of the overlying gas. These properties follow directly from Kirchhoff's laws of spectrum analysis (1858): (1) Incandescent solids, liquids, and gases under high pressure give a continuous spectrum. (2) Incandescent gases under low pressure give a discontinuous spectrum composed mainly of bright lines which show a characteristic number and wavelength depending on the substance vaporized. (3) When a continuous spectrum is passed through a gas, this gas absorbs light of a wavelength identical to its own bright-line spectrum.

Now according to these laws, a reversing layer which absorbs light to produce the Fraunhofer lines should show a bright-line spectrum corresponding to the Fraunhofer wavelengths when viewed separately. Such an observation is possible during a total solar eclipse when the Moon moves in front of the photosphere. This circumstance allows the chromosphere and corona to be viewed without the bright glare of the photosphere, and the bright-line *flash spectrum* was first observed by Young in 1870.

Thus, toward the end of the nineteenth century the following general summary of the solar atmosphere was given by Miss Clerke. (By permission from A. M. Clerke, A. Fowler, and J. E. Gore, "Astronomy," D. Appleton & Company, Inc., New York, 1898.)

> Starting from the photosphere, we meet first an envelope producing the *general* absorption, by which sunlight is enfeebled and reddened as if by the interposition of a slightly rufous shade. Next comes the reversing layer composed of mixed incandescent vapours, giving rise, by their *selective* absorption, to the Fraunhofer lines. No alterations in correspondence with the spot-cycle have yet been determined in either of these couches, which, close as they lie to the photosphere, remain, nevertheless, apparently indifferent to its agitations. They are overspread by the chromosphere and prominences; while above and beyond shines the mysterious corona; both chromosphere and corona strictly conforming, by manifest changes, to the sun's periodicity.

Investigations concerning the solar interior were also in progress during the nineteenth century, but a discussion of these is deferred until Section 1.4.

1.3 THE SUN AS A STAR AND EARLY IDEAS CONCERNING STELLAR SPECTRA

An event of great conceptual significance in astronomy was the conclusive establishment of the stars as self-luminous objects, basically similar to the Sun but seen as small, fixed points of light in the night sky by virtue of their great distance. Note that the problem here is to establish the hypothesis, not merely to hold it or speculate on it, which may have been done for centuries or possibly even millennia. It seems that one must establish two facts to be reasonably sure of the correspondence. (1) The distance must be measured to establish that the apparent brightnesses are in the correct ratio. (2) Some observations of the spectra of the star or stars should be made to establish the similar nature of emitted light (such as Fraunhofer lines; see Chapter 2) and thus presumably of the material emitting the light.

The first part requires an accurate parallax and a reasonably accurate apparent magnitude for the Sun (and obviously for the star in question—but the Sun is the problem). Table 1.1 shows three basically reliable parallaxes obtained circa 1838 by three separate observers, as given by van Biesbroeck. These numbers are the half-angle of the star's position as seen from opposite sides of the Earth's orbit. The principle was well known, and since the sixteenth century, Tycho, Roemer, Bradley, Herschel, and many others had looked for the parallactic shift. These efforts were not in vain since they resulted in Bradley's discovery of aberration and nutation and Herschel's discovery of true double stars; the problem was one of equipment. We should recall that astronomical photography did not exist and that the elaborate and standard reduction schemes as perfected by Schlesinger were yet to come.

Henderson's measurement was made with a meridian circle, W. Struve's with a micrometer, and Bessel's with a heliometer (which was an objective lens cut in half, one half being moved by means of a precision screw; angles between nearby stars were measured by bringing the two images into coincidences with the screw.) Parallax determinations are further discussed in Chapter 5. The approximate parallax given in Table 1.1 leads to the ratio of *apparent* brightnesses of the Sun and α Centauri of $10^{11}:1$. Recall (or see Chapter 5) that a factor of 10 in brightness corresponds to 2.5 mag to compute a magnitude difference of 27.5 mag. The modern values of $+0.3$ for α Centauri and -26.7 for the Sun give

TABLE 1.1   THE FIRST PARALLAXES*

OBSERVER	STAR	FIRST VALUE	MODERN VALUE
Henderson	α Cen	1″16	0″76
W. Struve	Vega	0″26	0″12
Bessel	61 Cyg	0″31	0″30

* From "Astrophysics" by J. A. Hynek (ed.). Copyright, 1951. McGraw-Hill Book Company. Used by permission.

27.0, which is close enough. Older values were rougher but quite sufficient.

The second crucial piece of evidence came in quite easily, since stellar spectra had been observed (visually) by Fraunhofer beginning in 1824 and by Huggins and Secchi in 1864. It was found that stellar spectra were basically absorption-line spectra (like the Sun) and that some stars, e.g., Capella and α Centauri, had spectra which closely resembled the spectra of the Sun.

Huggins studied a small number of stars thoroughly, with the aim of identifying elements. On the other hand, Secchi studied nearly four thousand spectra with the aim of establishing a classification scheme. Secchi divided his stars into four groups: (I) Stars with strong absorption lines of hydrogen such as Sirius; these comprised over half of his sample and correspond roughly to modern classes A and F. (II) Yellow stars with absorption spectra, such as the Sun and Capella; types I and II contained seven-eighths of Secchi's sample. Type II corresponds roughly to modern types G and K. (III) Red stars with bands (modern class M, bands due to TiO), like Betelgeuse; these comprise about one-eighth of the sample. (IV) Red stars like 19 Piscium with molecular bands; these stars are rare. They correspond to the modern class N, which is characterized by carbon bands. Classes III and IV were distinguished by the band structure.

Subsequent refinements of the scheme of spectral classification, such as the Harvard system, have shown that further classes are necessary, a fact which is not surprising. However, it was conclusively established that a large fraction of stellar spectra could be arranged into one continuous sequence, in which the character of the spectra changed gradually from class to class. The modern scheme of classification is discussed in Section 5.3.

1.4 EARLY IDEAS CONCERNING STELLAR STRUCTURE AND EVOLUTION

With the Sun-star correspondence established, let us now sketch some of the ideas concerning the structure and evolution of the stars. Dictionaries usually define the Sun as the incandescent body of gases about which the planets revolve. However, it was not always held that the Sun was mainly gaseous. W. Herschel held that the Sun was composed of solid rock, the luminous part being just a superficial covering. Sunspots were thought to be holes in the superficial layer; life on the Sun was considered possible. However, even the existing understanding of strength of materials should have indicated to Herschel that the solar interior was gaseous because of the great pressure to be expected. It was eventually realized and justified because of the high temperature that the perfect-gas law, $P = NkT$, was valid throughout the Sun; here, P is the pressure in dynes per square centimeter, N is the number of particles per cubic centimeter, T is the temperature in degrees Kelvin, and k $(= 1.4 \times 10^{-16}$ ergs/deg$)$ is Boltzmann's constant. Lane also speculated that collisions between atoms at high temperatures might tear them apart; this conjecture is remarkably close to our modern ideas concerning ionization in the solar interior.

The first quantitative model of the solar interior was obtained by Lane in 1869 under the assumption that the outward flow of energy was by convection. This assumption, although wrong, seemed natural, since it was easy to show that conduction was hopelessly inadequate. Incidentally, Lane's early solar, polytropic models had a perfectly reasonable value for the central temperature of about 10 million °K. The first steps toward a quantitative theory of the transport of energy by radiation date from the work of K. Schwarzschild in 1906. Modern astrophysics indicates that throughout most of the Sun energy transport is by radiation; nonetheless, convection is important in a relatively thin region just below the photosphere. This region is the hydrogen convection zone discussed in Chapter 2.

If we take as given that the interior of the Sun is a highly ionized gas in radiative equilibrium, then the outstanding problems are those of composition and the energy source. Until the 1930s, the Sun was taken to be gaseous but composed of metallic vapors; the Balmer lines were regarded as "skin phenomena." Finally, it became apparent from problems associated with the mass-luminosity relation (Chapter 4) that the equations could not work without the addition of large amounts of hydrogen (and later helium). Thus the Gordian knot was undone. Soon the nuclear reactions which basically transmute hydrogen into helium (with the energy release from the mass defect) were discovered. In 1939, Wildt suggested that the H⁻ ion (an ion composed of one proton and two electrons) was the source of opacity in the solar photosphere; this has been verified. It is hard to overemphasize the importance of the discovery of hydrogen as the main constituent of the stars.

The early studies of stars indicated that, roughly speaking, all stars could be divided into giants and dwarfs by using their radii as a criterion. An old idea concerning the formation of stars was that stars originate by a process of condensation from the interstellar gas; this idea is the heart of an early evolutionary scheme due to H. N. Russell. The newly formed stars would be large and relatively cool; as the star continues its contraction, the radius decreases and the temperature increases until the star resembles a dwarf. From here on, the star remains nearly the same size but cools because of energy loss to space. The theory depended on gravitational contraction for an energy source. This theory was abandoned by H. N. Russell during his own lifetime when it was realized that only the transformation of hydrogen into heavier elements could supply the solar energy requirements for the times required by the geological evidence.

Modern theories of evolution, strongly based on nuclear energy sources, are discussed in Chapter 6.

* 2 * the solar
atmosphere

Basic Facts

The photosphere is the region from which we receive the major portion of the solar energy output in the form of optical radiation (say from 4,000 to 7,000 Å). At the Earth we receive some 1.95 cal/(cm²)(min); this figure leads to the effective temperature quoted in Chapter 1 of 5750°K. The general run of the solar emission is shown in Figure 2.1. As is well known, the solar spectrum contains localized regions of wavelength of greatly reduced intensity, the Fraunhofer lines.

The photosphere is not a region of energy generation; this occurs deep in the interior. Rather, the photosphere receives a flux of radiant energy from below and, so to speak, "reshuffles" it into the observed emergent spectrum. The nature of the photosphere and the physical principles which are important in understanding the emergent radiation are the subject of this section.

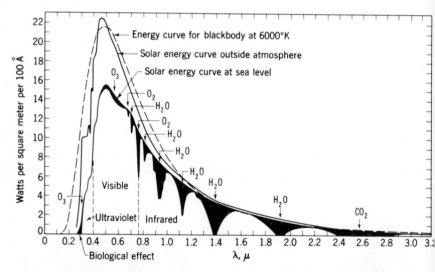

FIGURE 2.1   The spectral energy curve of the Sun at sea level and extrapolated outside the atmosphere, as given by E. Pettit. *From Astrophysics by J. A. Hynek (ed.). Copyright, 1951. McGraw-Hill Book Company. Used by permission.*

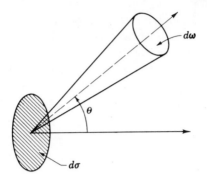

FIGURE 2.2   A schematic illustration of the quantities used in defining the specific intensity; see Equation (2.2) and the text for discussion.

The Equation of Transfer

If we are to fully utilize the solar radiation as a tool for studying the photosphere, we must have some elementary conception of how radiation is transported through a medium. The starting point is the equation of transfer,

$$\frac{dI_v}{ds} = -\rho K_v I_v + j_v \rho \qquad (2.1)$$

The various definitions are as follows: s is the linear distance in the medium and ρ is the density in the medium; I_v is the specific intensity or intensity and is defined by

$$dE = I_v \cos\theta \, d\omega \, dv \, dt \, d\sigma \qquad (2.2)$$

where dE_v (per unit frequency interval dv) is the radiant energy in a cone of solid angle $d\omega$ passing through a surface of area $d\sigma$ in time dt and where θ is the angle between the cone and the normal to the surface (see Figure 2.2). Thus, I_v has dimensions of ergs/(cm)^2(sec)(steradian)(unit frequency interval); when interpreted as a surface brightness, I_v clearly does not depend on the distance of the observer. For example, a specific area on the

Sun when viewed from a specific direction has an I_ν independent of the distance (assuming no complicating effects between here and the Sun). Lastly, K_ν and j_ν are the mass absorption and mass emission coefficients, respectively. The radiation removed from a pencil beam is

$$K_\nu I_\nu \, dm \, d\nu \, d\omega \, dt \qquad (2.3)$$

to define the absorption coefficient, and the amount of energy emitted into the solid angle is $d\omega$ is

$$j_\nu \, dm \, d\omega \, d\nu \, dt \qquad (2.4)$$

to define the emission coefficient. Hence, we can now see that the change in the intensity (dI_ν) in a cylinder of length ds is simply the excess of emission $(j_\nu \rho)$ over absorption $(-\rho K_\nu I_\nu)$. This is the physical interpretation of Equation (2.1).

Immediately, we must clarify some of the terminology used. Absorption as used above means both true absorption and scattering. Think of the absorbing atom as a black box. We say a photon is absorbed if it goes into the black box and does not reappear reasonably near its original frequency. We say that scattering has occurred if the black box keeps the photon for a short time and sends it off in another direction with essentially its original frequency.

Two more quantities which are useful in the discussion of the equation of transfer are the source function,

$$\mathcal{J}_\nu = \frac{j_\nu}{K_\nu} \qquad (2.5)$$

and the optical thickness or opacity,

$$\tau_\nu = \int_z^\infty K_\nu \, \rho \, dz \qquad (2.6)$$

Here the opacity is written for the case of a plane-parallel atmosphere with axial symmetry; note that τ_ν is zero at the top of an atmosphere and increases as one moves inward and that z is measured as increasing along the outward normal to the upper

boundary of the atmosphere (see Figure 2.3). If we now let θ be
the angle between the cone of radiation and the outward normal
(i.e., the positive z-axis) and if we set $\mu = \cos\theta$, Equations (2.1),
(2.5), and (2.6) give the equation of transfer in its standard
form, viz.,

$$\mu \frac{dI_\nu}{d\tau_\nu} = I_\nu - \mathcal{J}_\nu \tag{2.7}$$

The source function $\mathcal{J}_\nu$ has two limiting cases of considerable
interest. For the case of local thermodynamic equilibrium (LTE),
the source function is equal to the Planck function, i.e.,

$$\mathcal{J}_\nu = B_\nu(T) = \frac{2h\nu^3}{c^2} \frac{1}{e^{h\nu/kT}-1} \tag{2.8}$$

where h = Planck's constant = 6.6×10^{-27} erg-sec
ν = frequency, sec^{-1}
c = velocity of light in a vacuum = 3.0×10^{10} cm/sec
T = temperature, °K
k = Boltzmann's constant = 1.4×10^{-16} erg/deg
Here there is no scattering; all the radiation is thermal in origin.
For the case of pure, isotropic scattering,

$$\mathcal{J}_\nu = \frac{1}{4\pi} \int_{4\pi} I_\nu \, d\omega \tag{2.9}$$

Here the source function is equal to the average or mean intensity.
There are several detailed methods for solving Equation (2.7),
all of which are outside the scope of this book. A formal solution
can be effected by noting that Equation (2.7) is a linear first-
order differential equation which has a known solution. For the
case of the radiation emerging from the top of an atmosphere,
dropping the subscripts ν, and writing t for the opacity as the
variable of integration, we have

the solar atmosphere

31940   523.013
        B821

Brescia College Library
Owensboro, Kentucky

$$I(0,+\mu) = \int\limits_0^\infty \mathcal{J}(t,+\mu)e^{-t/\mu}\frac{dt}{\mu} \qquad \text{(2.10)}$$

Physically, this equation states that the emergent radiation is composed of the contribution from each level $[\mathcal{J}(t,+\mu)]$, which is then reduced by the intervening opacity $(e^{-t/\mu})$.

Structure of the Photosphere

The solution of the equation of transfer just given is of no particular value unless we know or can interpret $\mathcal{J}(t,+\mu)$. When some of the more complex methods of radiative transfer are applied to the photosphere, it is possible to compute $\mathcal{J}(t,+\mu)$ and thus to predict the features of the solar spectrum. Here we try the inverse approach.

It is well known that the assumption of LTE [Equation (2.8)] is quite reasonable for many applications. Hence, Equation (2.10) becomes

$$I(0,+\mu) = \int\limits_0^\infty B(T)e^{-t/\mu}\frac{dt}{\mu} \qquad \text{(2.11)}$$

Since $I(0,+\mu)$ is observed, for example, in the limb-darkening observations (see just below and Chapter 1), it is possible to compute the temperature as a function of τ, that is, a T-τ relation.

Let us illustrate the solution by considering qualitatively the question of limb darkening—namely, what can we infer from the fact that the Sun in visual wavelengths is brighter at the center of the disk $[I(0,1)]$ than near the limb $[I(0,0.2)$, say]? From Equation (2.11) and the properties of the exponential function, we note that little radiation is received from points along the ray deeper than $t/\mu = 1$; in other words, we see essentially down to unit slant opacity. (Note: the slant opacity is computed along the line of sight, which is not the case for the opacity defined in Equation 2.6; this latter opacity is counted along the normal to the surface.) This means that at the center of the disk $\mu = 1$, we see down to an opacity of 1. But, at $\mu = 0.2$, the normal opacity is only 0.2 at a slant opacity of 1. Hence, the observations

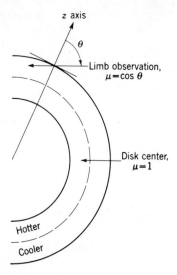

FIGURE 2.3 A schematic illustration of the solar limb darkening and the coordinate system described in the text.

near the solar limb refer to regions higher in the atmosphere; these higher regions are fainter and cooler than the brighter, hotter regions probed by the center of the disk observations. The situation is illustrated schematically in Figure 2.3. Thus, we have established that the temperature of the Sun increases as one moves inward. The exact values of $I(0,+\mu)$ give the values of the temperature and their variation.

If we consider a T-τ relation established, we now seek the additional equations necessary for the specification of the structure of the photosphere. Let us write the T-τ relation in terms of a suitably defined mean optical depth. Then, Equation (2.6) becomes

$$dr = -\bar{K}\rho \, dz \qquad \text{(2.12)}$$

The equation of hydrostatic equilibrium is

$$dP = -g\rho \, dz \qquad \text{(2.13)}$$

where P is the total gas pressure and g is the gravitational acceleration at the point in question. The last two equations yield

$$\frac{dP}{d\tau} = \frac{g}{\bar{K}} \qquad \textbf{(2.14)}$$

Therefore, we can establish a P-τ relation *if* we can specify the
mean absorption coefficient at each point; for years, the problem
remained unsolved until R. Wildt suggested that the opacity in the
solar atmosphere was due mainly to bound-free absorption by the
H^- atom.

Thus, so far as the solar continuum is concerned, photons travel
through the photosphere via the reactions

(absorption) $\qquad\qquad h\nu + H^- \rightarrow H + e \qquad\qquad$ **(2.15)**

(emission) $\qquad\qquad H + e \rightarrow h\nu + H^- \qquad\qquad$ **(2.16)**

Symbolically, absorption occurs when a photon ($h\nu$; h is Planck's
constant and ν is the frequency of the photon) ionizes the H^- ion
(composed of one proton and two electrons) and produces a free
electron and a neutral hydrogen atom [Equation (2.15)]. The
recombination of a hydrogen atom and an electron produces a
photon ($h\nu$) and an H^- ion [Equation (2.16)]. The two photons
shown in Equations (2.15) and (2.16) need not have the same
energy. The bound-free absorption of H^- is important from about
3,500 to 16,500 Å; free-free absorption is important for wavelengths longer than 16,500 Å. Of course, other absorbing con-
stituents and absorption lines (called the *blanketing effect*) are
important for accurate numerical calculations.

Thus, while the effective temperature of the Sun is established
by the rate of energy generation in the interior, the spectral form
of the solar emission is determined by the fact that photons are
transmitted through the photosphere via the H^- atom.

If H^- is the dominant absorbing constituent in the solar photosphere, we must proceed to calculate the abundance of H^- per
gram of solar material or, more conveniently, the number of H^-
ions per neutral hydrogen atom. This quantity can be calculated
from known atomic constants by means of the Saha equation (see
Chapter 5) *if* the temperature and electron pressure are known;
this situation arises because the Saha equation takes the form

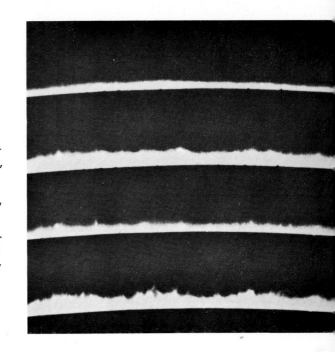

FIGURE 2.8 The chromosphere with its spicular structure. Sacramento Peak Observatory, Air Force Cambridge Research Laboratories. From "Science in Space" by L. V. Berkner and H. Odishaw (Eds.). Copyright 1961. McGraw-Hill Book Company. Used by permission.

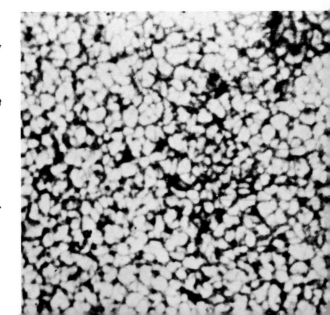

FIGURE 2.9 Solar granulation photograph taken on August 17, 1959, with a balloon-borne telescope. Scale: 1 cm on print = 4600 km on Sun. By permission from Project Stratoscope of Princeton University, sponsored by the Office of Naval Research, the National Science Foundation, and the National Aeronautics and Space Administration.

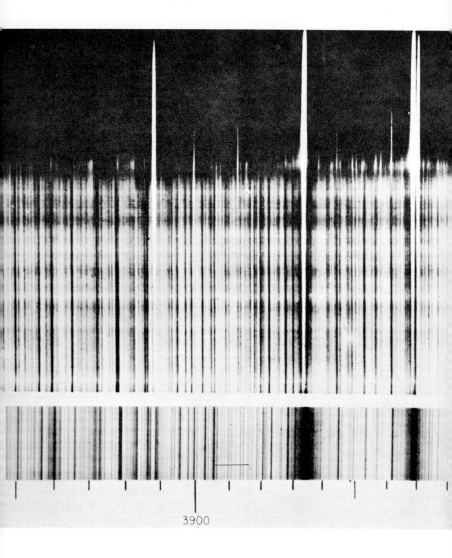

3900

FIGURE 2.10   The spectrum of the chromosphere or flash spectrum (top) near 3900 A with the photospheric spectrum included for comparison (bottom). Notice the reversal (positive print). By permission from the Lick Observatory.

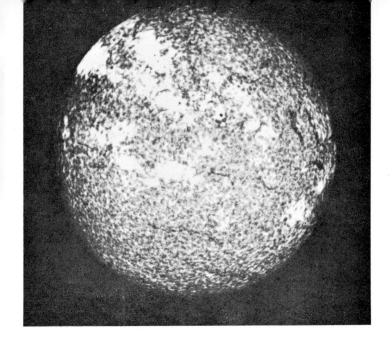

FIGURE 2.11   A CaII (K₃ = central emission core of the K line) spectroheliogram clearly showing the mottling and the chromospheric network. By permission from the Observatoire de Paris-Meudon.

FIGURE 2.12   The intermediate corona. By permission from G. van Biesbroeck.

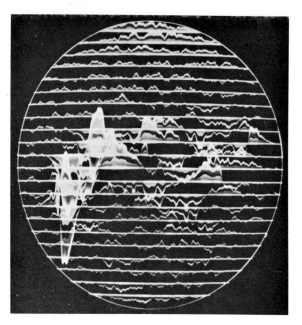

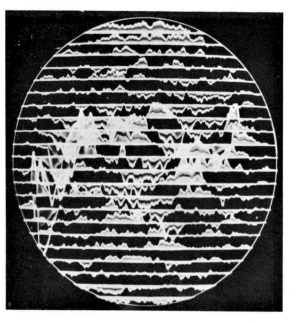

FIGURE 3.1   These magnetic maps of the sun's disk show the location, field intensity, and polarity of weak magnetic fields in the photosphere of the sun, apart from sunspots. The records are made automatically by a scanning system that employs a polarizing analyzer, a powerful spectrograph, and a sensitive photoelectric detector for measuring the longitudinal component of the magnetic field by means of the Zeeman effect. A deflection of one trace interval corresponds to a field of about one gauss. The small deflections of opposite magnetic polarity near the North and South poles are indicative of the sun's "general magnetic field." The extended fields near the equator arise from characteristic "BM" (Bipolar Magnetic) regions that sometimes produce spots. North is at top, east at right. Courtesy H. W. Babcock, Mount Wilson and Palomar Observatories.

$N(H) N_e/N(H^-) = f(T)$. Here, $N(H)$, N_e, and $N(H^-)$ are the number of hydrogen atoms, electrons, and negative hydrogen ions per cubic centimeter, respectively. Now we know T from the T-τ relation, and hence only N_e remains to be specified. The electrons in the photosphere come mainly from the metals—Mg, Si, Fe, Ca, Al, and Na—which are all singly ionized. Hence, if A is the ratio of hydrogen to metals by number, then $P_e/P = 1/A$, and the electron pressure is specified.

Since $\bar{K}$ is known as a function of $P(P_e)$ and $\tau(T)$, Equation (2.14) can be integrated to give a P-τ relation. Then, the density is known from the perfect-gas law (Chapters 1 and 4), and Equation (2.12) can be integrated to establish the geometrical depth as a function of the optical depth. Therefore, in principle, we can obtain a model of the solar photosphere; the results of a detailed calculation by A. Unsöld are shown in Table 2.1. Information concerning other regions of the Sun is found in the table; these regions will be discussed in due course.

The Fraunhofer Lines

In broad outline, the Fraunhofer lines in the Sun and the corresponding phenomena in other stars have their origin in selective absorption by atomic and molecular species. These absorptions can, for convenience, be idealized as true absorptions or scatterings; under conditions thought to prevail in stellar atmospheres, an *absorption line* results in either case.

Consider the energy level or Grotrian diagram for the neutral sodium atom, shown in Figure 2.4. The scale in electron volts shows the energy difference between the various states of the atom; normally the atom is found in the state of the lowest energy, called the ground state. The transitions corresponding to the well-known yellow D lines of sodium, $\lambda 5,890$ and $\lambda 5,896$, are marked in the figure. These energies required for the D lines are not exact. The states of the sodium atom are broadened in energy mainly by the thermal doppler motions of the absorbing atoms (macroscopic) and, from Heisenberg's uncertainty principle, by the finite time spent by the electron in the upper or excited state (microscopic).

TABLE 2.1   A MODEL SOLAR ATMOSPHERE*

HEIGHT z, km	SOLAR RADII	TEMPERATURE T, °K	GAS PRESSURE, dynes/cm² log P	ELECTRON PRESSURE, dynes/cm² log P_e
1,400,000	3.0	$2 \cdot 10^6$	−3.8	−4.1
700,000	2.0	$2 \cdot 10^6$	−2.8	−3.1
350,000	1.50	$2 \cdot 10^6$	−2.1	−2.4
42,000	1.06	$2 \cdot 10^6$	−0.9	−1.2
20,000	1.03	$2 \cdot 10^6$	−0.8	−1.1
		↕ Very inhomogeneous		
3,000		⌢ 4000–6000	0.2	−1.7
2,000	* * *	⌢ 4000–6000	0.5	−1.4
1,000		⌢ 4000–6000	1.2	−0.9
	Opt. depth τ_{5000}			
Solar limb: 0	0.005	4090	4.1	−0.5
	0.01	4295	4.3	−0.3
	0.05	4855	4.6	+0.2
	0.1	5030	4.8	+0.4
	0.5	5805	5.1	1.2
−260	1.0	6400	5.2	1.8
	2.0	7180	5.3	2.4
−280	* * *	10^4	5.3	4.0
	Solar radii			
−16,000	−0.02	10^5	9.4	9.1
−140,000	−0.2	10^6	12.3	12.0

* By permission from A. Unsöld, in "Space Age Astronomy," ed. A. J. Deutsch and W. B. Klemperer, Academic Press, New York, 1962.

However, lines in the solar spectrum are usually not much wider than 1 Å. Hence, the probability of absorption, which is greatest at the center of the line, is substantially decreased at 1 Å from the line center and is zero for almost all practical purposes 10 Å from the line center. The exact calculation of absorption cross sections and line widths (other than thermal) is a problem of quantum mechanics; we note that other influences can be important in determining the line shape, such as collisions with other atoms, magnetic fields (Zeeman effect, important in sunspots; see Chapter 3), and electric fields (Stark effect).

Let us now consider two idealized cases of line formation in the

ELECTRONS/cm^3 log N_e	TURBULENT VELOCITY V_t, km/sec	LAYER	MAIN ENERGY TRANSFER
5.5			
6.4			
7.2		Corona	Thermal
8.4			conduction
8.5			
	~15	Transition layer	Mechanical
10.5			energy
10.8	12	Chromosphere	Radiation
11.3	7		
11.7	1–2		
12.0			
12.4			
12.6			
13.3	2	Photosphere	Radiation
13.8			
14.4			
15.86	2	Hydrogen convection zone	Convection
20.0	0.3		
21.9	0.0		Radiation

Sun. First, we discuss the formation of lines in local thermodynamic equilibrium, where any photons absorbed by the atom are considered lost. Here the absorption by the atom simply increases the opacity near the appropriate wavelength. Refer now to Equation (2.11) and recall the qualitative explanation of limb darkening. In a like manner, the extra selective absorption increases the opacity in the line, and an observer sees to a much higher level in the photosphere in the line than he does in the neighboring continuum. Since the temperature in the photosphere increases inward, the continuum arises from a deeper, hotter, and hence brighter

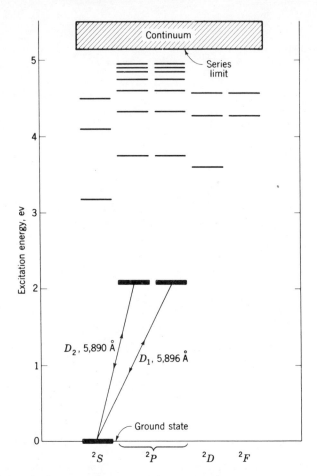

FIGURE 2.4   An energy level or Grotrian diagram for neutral sodium, Na I. Many states near the continuum are not shown.

region than does the radiation of the characteristic wavelength; the result is an absorption line. Notice, however, that no absorption line would result on this picture for an isothermal atmosphere.

However, a completely different explanation, based entirely on *continuous absorption* and *selective scattering*, can be given. For selective scattering, photons *away* from the characteristic wavelength pass through the photosphere unaffected by selective scattering. However, photons near the characteristic frequency are scattered (namely absorbed and reemitted) in a random direction, and thus these specific photons travel upward through the photosphere in random walk style, i.e., with the path length required to traverse the photosphere increased compared with that of the continuum photons. This increase in path length greatly increases the probability of continuous absorption (say by H⁻) of these photons, and the absorption line appears in the emergent spectrum. This mechanism does not depend on a proper temperature gradient in the photosphere.

These two mechanisms serve to illustrate the general principles involved in line formation; in practice, the physical details of the absorption and reemission must be specified and the appropriate transfer equation solved. While some problems of line formation require further investigation, the theory and observation are in substantial agreement.

Solar Abundances

The abundances of the elements in stars are of prime interest in the study of stellar spectra and in the study of stellar evolution. The abundances of the elements in the interior of a star may be different from the atmosphere because of the nuclear transformation of the elements in the interior; however, it is generally thought that the atmospheric abundances are a good approximation to the initial abundances (before alteration by nuclear reactions) throughout the stars, and, in any event, these abundances are the only ones relevant to stellar astronomy that are directly determinable.

Since the Fraunhofer lines in the solar spectrum are formed because of selective absorption by atomic species, it is clear that abundances can be determined from them. Note, however, that some elements, notably helium, have no absorption lines in the solar spectrum suitable for an abundance determination.

In principle, the abundance of an element can be determined from the observation of one line, such as one of the D lines of sodium. The measurement can consist of the quantity $r_\nu = I_\nu(0,\mu)/I_c(0,\mu)$, called the residual intensity (defined in Figure 2.5). However, the total area of the absorption lines measured relative to the continuum is obtained with greater accuracy; this quantity,

$$W_\lambda = \int (1 - r_\lambda) \, d\lambda \qquad \text{(2.17)}$$

is called the equivalent width.

To specify the mode and amount of line formation, we need a model of the photosphere—taken, presumably, from continuum studies. Consider then the formation of one of the D lines of neutral sodium. At each height we need to know what fraction of sodium is unionized and in the ground state (see Figure 2.4). To obtain the fraction unionized we use the Saha equation (see Section 5.6), and we specify the ionization temperature (T in the Saha equation). To obtain the fraction of neutral sodium in the ground state we use the Boltzmann formula (see Section 5.6), and we specify the excitation temperature (T in the Boltzmann formula). Normally these "temperatures" and the temperature appearing in the Planck formula are the same, namely, the temperature specified by the photospheric model. When this is true, local thermodynamic equilibrium exists, and we shall consider that this is the case here. Hence, with all physical parameters specified and the model photosphere chosen, we need only vary the abundance of the element until an absorption line of the proper equivalent width is obtained.

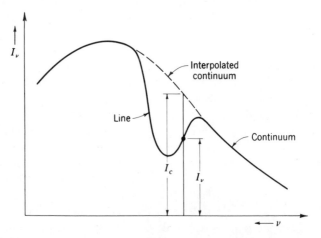

FIGURE 2.5   A schematic diagram showing the quantities used in defining r_ν and the equivalent width. *From Solar System Astrophysics by J. C. Brandt and P. Hodge. Copyright, 1964. McGraw-Hill Book Company. Used by permission.*

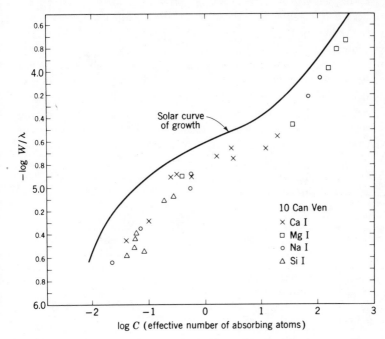

FIGURE 2.6   The solar curve of growth as described in the text. Also shown are the points for certain metals in the star 10 Canus Venaticorum; these metals are underabundant relative to the Sun by a factor of 2 to 3. *Courtesy of G. Wallerstein, University of Washington.*

In practice, it is usually risky to determine an abundance from the study of one line, and one uses many lines through the artifice of the *curve of growth*, which describes the way the equivalent width varies with the effective abundance. In the laboratory, the effective abundance can be changed for a single line simply by increasing the number of atoms in the absorbing path length. When this is done, one finds that at first W_λ is directly proportional to the abundance, then the curve levels off, and finally W_λ increases as the square root of the abundance. This type of behavior occurs because the absorption at first occurs mainly near the line center, and the addition of more atoms simply means a corresponding increase in the absorption; however, soon all the light at the center of the line is absorbed (called saturation), and the only way W_λ can be increased is to absorb *away* from the line center, a process which increases W_λ relatively slowly.

In stellar atmospheres, the curve of growth occurs because the various lines of the same element have different strengths. Hence, the curve of growth takes the form of a plot of $\log W_\lambda/\lambda$ versus $\log C$, where C contains all factors (atomic constants, temperatures, etc.) *except* abundance factors. The difference between the observed and computed curves of growth yields the abundance of the element in question. The curve of growth for the Sun is shown in Figure 2.6. Some sample abundance determinations are given in Figure 2.7.

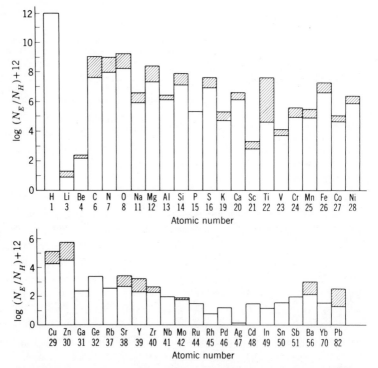

FIGURE 2.7   The logarithms of the solar abundances relative to hydrogen. The shaded areas correspond to the spread in the published determinations.

Introduction

The chromosphere takes its name from its orange-red appearance at solar eclipses. During a total eclipse of the Sun it can be seen with the naked eye as a faint colored ring surrounding the dark outline of the moon. It is a region of great inhomogeneity and contrasts. The chromosphere is at most a few tens of thousands of kilometers thick, but it is bounded below by the upper layers of the photosphere at some 5000°K and above by the corona with temperatures reaching 10^{6}°K and above. The heterogeneous nature is emphasized by the simultaneous existence of emission of CN and the λ7,892 coronal line of Fe XI; this immediately leads one to suspect that the chromosphere may be composed of hot and cold elements. Details of the chromosphere are to be found in our summary model.

When the chromosphere is observed under favorable conditions at a solar eclipse, it shows a fine, hairlike structure, which has been likened to a burning prairie. The lower part of the chromosphere appears as a homogeneous layer from which emerge the bright streamers called spicules (see Figure 2.8). The spicules last for a few minutes and extend some 10,000 km above the limb. Spicules are found all over the Sun, do not seem to be related to solar activity, and may well be related to the problem of heating and support of the chromosphere.

Chromospheric Heating

The temperature increases outward in the chromosphere and hence it cannot be regarded as a simple extension of the photosphere. Two energy sources are available: (1) mechanical energy in the form of wave motion (spicules?) and (2) conduction from the corona. Since it is believed that the corona also is heated by mechanical energy, let us also consider its possible origin.

Mechanical energy is currently considered to be produced in the hydrogen convection zone due to convective instability (see

Table 2.1); this energy flux is but a minute fraction of the radiant flux in the photosphere. How does convective instability occur? Consider a perturbation in the form of a small bubble of material in the Sun which we move upward a small distance δr. If this is done rapidly so that the bubble does not exchange heat with the surrounding gas, then the process is described as adiabatic. The change in temperature of the bubble is simply $\delta r \left| \frac{dT}{dr} \right|_{ad}$, where $\left| \frac{dT}{dr} \right|_{ad}$ is the adiabatic temperature gradient which is appropriate to the case where the decrease of internal energy is equal to the external work performed by the bubble. Similarly, the surrounding material has a temperature difference of $\delta r \left| \frac{dT}{dr} \right|_{str}$, where $\left| \frac{dT}{dr} \right|_{str}$ is the structural gradient in the star. If

$$\left| \frac{dT}{dr} \right|_{str} > \left| \frac{dT}{dr} \right|_{ad} \qquad \text{(2.18)}$$

the bubble cools less than its surroundings, and since it remains in pressure equilibrium with the surroundings, must be less dense. For this case, the buoyancy force continues to push the bubble upward, and an instability results. Equation (2.18) is usually called the Schwarzschild condition for convective instability. Note that the opposite condition favors stability.

We now know that the Schwarzschild instability criterion is satisfied below the photosphere, and hence we expect the convective transport of energy to be important in this region. This situation exists below the photosphere because of an increase in the opacity which reduces the "mixing" due to photons and allows the existence of the high temperature gradient responsible for the convection. By analogy with classical studies of convection, we expect a cellular flow pattern—say with hot gases rising in the middle of the cell and the cool gases sinking at the cell boundary. The solar granulation, clearly shown in Figure 2.9, is apparently the result of the penetration of these cellular motions into the photosphere. The photosphere is actually a region of constant change and considerable unrest. The "chaotic" picture does not show in "still" photographs of the Sun, but movies of the photosphere show it quite clearly.

The Reynolds number is a dimensionless number that governs the conditions for turbulence to take place in the flow of gas. The flow is found to be turbulent when the Reynolds number exceeds a certain critical value. The Reynolds number can be computed for the convective motions; it is so large that the flow must be turbulent. The importance of turbulent motions is that they produce mechanical noise, in the form of acoustic waves which travel at the velocity of sound. The upward flux of such mechanical noise (analogous to sound waves) is

$$F_{\text{mech}} = \frac{1}{2}\, \rho\,(v_t)^2\, v_s \qquad (2.19)$$

where ρ = density
   v_t = amplitude of the material velocity
         of the wave or disturbance
   v_s = velocity of sound

If there is no dissipation and F_{mech} (the flux of mechanical energy) remains constant, then v_t must increase rapidly to balance the very rapid decrease of ρ in the solar atmosphere. Eventually, v_t becomes on the order of v_s, shock waves are generated, and energy deposition is the result. It is this deposition of mechanical energy which is responsible for the maintenance of the chromosphere and corona at temperatures higher than the boundary temperature.

The scheme sketched here is probably correct in principle, but it neglects at least one important complication, the presence of the solar magnetic field. Noise generation and energy deposition seem to be enhanced when a magnetic field is present. Also, proper account must be taken of the various hybrid magneto-acoustic waves which arise under these circumstances.

Chromospheric Spectra and Support

A sample of the spectrum of the chromosphere is shown in Figure 2.10; the same wavelength region of the photospheric spectrum is shown for comparison. Notice that the two spectra are almost reversals of each other; lines which show in absorption in the photospheric spectrum (such as the H and K lines of ionized calcium, Ca II) appear in emission in the chromospheric spectrum.

The detailed interpretation of the chromospheric spectrum for the determination of temperatures and densities is beyond the scope of this treatise; however, some typical results are shown in Table 2.1. The radio results have been used in constructing such models.

The study of spectra taken at solar eclipses can give valuable information concerning the height distribution of chromospheric material. The various emission lines shown in Figure 2.10 are of different lengths and therefore correspond to different heights in the chromosphere. By observing the way the *total* emission in a given line (or lines of the same element) above the limb of the Moon varies during a solar eclipse, it is possible to determine the height distribution of the emitting matter in the chromosphere. At least in the lower parts of the chromosphere, the conditions leading to the emission of the various lines are relatively constant with height, and hence, the height distribution of emitting matter should be representative of the actual distribution of matter in the chromosphere.

The results can be represented in terms of the emission gradient β defined by

$$\frac{N}{N_0} = e^{-\beta x} \qquad (2.20)$$

where N = density at x

x = height in the chromosphere

N_0 = density at $x = 0$

Note that $H = \beta^{-1}$ is called the *scale height*.

The results from many studies of eclipse data indicate that β is within a factor of 2 of 1.5×10^{-8}/cm *for all elements observed from hydrogen to iron.*

Consider that the chromosphere is isothermal and that it has turbulent velocities which can be represented by a gaussian distribution. Then, we have

$$\beta = \frac{g}{(k\,T/m) + (v_t{}^2/2)} \qquad (2.21)$$

where g = solar acceleration of gravity

k = Boltzmann's constant ($= 1.38 \times 10^{-16}$ erg/deg)

T = temperature

m = mass of the particle that forms the gas

v_t = turbulent velocity

We see immediately (assuming $v_t = 0$) that the elements in the chromosphere do not follow emission gradients appropriate to each individual species, since then β for iron would be 56 times the β for hydrogen. Still assuming $v_t = 0$, we find that complete mixing does not fit the observations, since representative compositions give a mean mass [m in Equation (2.21)] of 1.3 times the mass of the hydrogen atom; this gives a β which is some 5 to 6 times larger than the observational value.

If, however, we take $v_t = 15$ km/sec, then $\beta = 2 \times 10^{-8}$/cm follows, in agreement with the observations. It is probably not a coincidence that this value of v_t is in the range expected from Equation (2.19) and the chromospheric densities and temperatures. The calculation referred to in the last sentence starts with a model of the convective motions which then leads to a calculation of the mechanical (acoustic) energy flux F_{mech} generated in the hydrogen convection zone. If there is no dissipation, F_{mech} is a constant, and the density ρ and sound velocity v_s can be computed from a model of the chromosphere; thus v_t can be determined as a function of height in the chromosphere (see the summary model, Table 2.1).

Hence, the rough sketch of the problem of chromospheric support is consistent with our discussion concerning the generation of mechanical noise and the heating of the chromosphere and corona.

The Fine Structure

The chromosphere is very inhomogeneous in the horizontal direction, besides the vertical direction. The chromospheric inhomogeneities can be observed very well on photographs of the Sun taken in essentially one wavelength, called spectroheliograms. In Figure 2.11 we show a K_3 spectroheliogram (taken in the central emission core of the K line of Ca II). From studies of such photographs three scales of fine structure are known: (1) The bright elements or fine mottling with characteristic dimensions $\sim 10^3$ km. The fine mottles seem to cluster together to form (2) the coarse mottling with characteristic diameters $\sim 5 \times 10^3$ km. The coarse mottles, in turn, appear to be arranged in a coarse network called (3) the chromospheric network, which has a mesh-width of roughly 40,000 km.

The theory of the chromospheric network seems related to the problem of the faculae and photospheric mass motions. See the discussion at the end of Section 3.4.

2.3 THE CORONA

Description

The corona is observable at the time of a total eclipse as a pearly light (comparable in brightness to the full Moon) which extends to several solar radii. It is generally taken to begin at 1.03 $R_\odot$, but the region immediately above this height may more properly belong to the region of extreme change between the chromosphere and corona; some workers have advocated the separate name of "transition zone" for this region. At very large distances from the Sun, the corona is called the interplanetary medium and is observed as the solar wind.

We now know that the corona is an essentially completely ionized gas at a temperature of 1 to 2×10^6 °K with electron densities of $10^9/cm^3$ or less (see the summary model, Table 2.1). Considerably fine structure is observed, and it is apparent that magnetic fields (as exemplified by the polar filaments; see Figure 2.12) are important in the corona. Because the light from the photosphere is so bright (see Figure 2.14), it is necessary to observe the corona at a solar eclipse, to use special devices equipped with occulting disks (such as the coronagraph), or to utilize radio observations. The latter are particularly valuable, since refraction of radio waves in the corona effectively shields the photosphere from the observer; this effect is shown in Figure 2.13.

The general structure of the corona is rather complex as judged from photographs of the corona taken at total eclipses of the Sun. Any long extensions of the corona are called streamers; these, in turn, can be subdivided into fans and rays. The latter are the small-scale features such as the polar rays which show the characteristic curvature suggestive of a dipole magnetic field. The rays over facular areas (see Section 3.4) are straight.

The fans are the large streamers with dimensions on the order

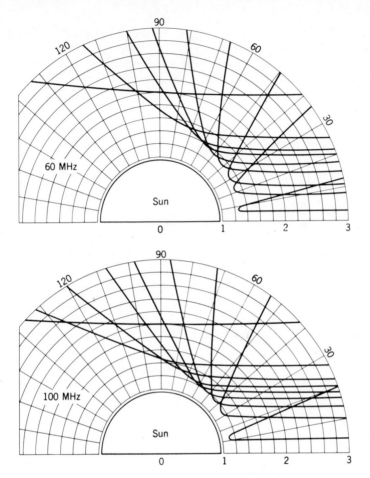

FIGURE 2.13   Radio-frequency ray paths in the corona at two frequencies (Jaeger and Westfold). *From Radio Astronomy by J. L. Steinberg
and J. Lequeux. Copyright, 1963. McGraw-Hill Book Company. Used by
permission.*

of 1 $R_\odot$ and larger; they are associated with quiescent prominences.
The distribution of fans at any particular time determines the
large-scale appearance of the corona which varies through the solar
cycle (see Chapter 3). At solar minimum, the solar activity is
concentrated toward the equator, and so are the fans responsible

for the appearance of the corona; at solar minimum, the corona shows considerable flattening. At solar maximum, activity is considerable and widespread, with the result that the corona is nearly circular in appearance. The corona shown in Figure 2.12 is an intermediate form.

The Coronal Light

The pearly coronal light is composed of three physically distinct components: (1) the K corona, which is continuum radiation physically resulting from the scattering (Thomson) of photospheric radiation by free electrons in the corona. (2) the F corona, which is photospheric radiation diffracted by interplanetary dust. This component is not physically connected with the corona, but its determination is important since it must be subtracted from the observations to give radiation referring only to the corona. (3) the E or emission corona, which is simply the sum of the emission lines of the corona. The magnitudes of these various components and their variation with heliocentric distance are shown in Figure 2.14.

We return to the K corona in the discussion of the coronal electron densities. Briefly now we consider the coronal emission lines. There are several bright emission lines which come from the corona; their wavelengths do not coincide with the Fraunhofer lines, and for years these lines were attributed to the hypothetical element "coronium." Unfortunately, there is no place for "coronium" in the Periodic Table of the Elements. The mystery was solved by Grotrian and Edlén, who showed that the observed emission lines came from atoms which had been ionized many times. For example, the coronal green line, $\lambda 5,303$, comes from iron ionized 13 times (Fe XIV), the yellow line, $\lambda 5,694$, comes from Ca XV, and the red line, $\lambda 6,375$, comes from Fe X. These lines require low densities to appear, and the highly ionized atoms require a high temperature; these conditions are satisfied in the corona. The first condition is necessary because these lines originate from excited states with longer than normal lifetimes. A high density would allow these states to be depopulated by collisions with other atoms. The second condition is necessary because the ionization potentials are very high, up to several hundred electron

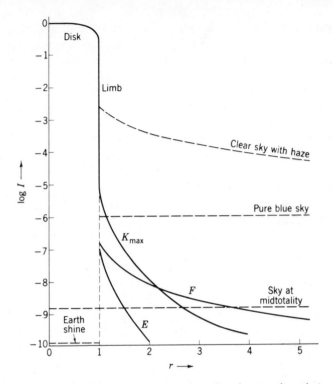

FIGURE 2.14   A figure, due to van de Hulst, showing the relative intensities of the components of coronal light: K_{max} is the continuous light due to electron scattering at solar maximum; F is the inner zodiacal light; E is the combined light of emission lines. *By permission from* The Sun, *G. P. Kuiper (ed.). Copyright, 1953, by the University of Chicago, published by the University of Chicago Press.*

volts; high temperatures ($\sim 10^6 \, °K$) are required if there are to be substantial numbers of electrons energetically capable of ionizing these atoms to such a great extent. Note that ionization in the corona occurs by electron impact and not by photons.

Densities

The coronal densities follow directly from observations of coronal brightness after the F corona and the radiation scattered in the

Earth's atmosphere have been subtracted to give the pure K corona. Since the radiation from the photosphere has well-known properties, and since the cross section for electron (Thomson) scattering is known (6.6×10^{-25} cm^2), the computation of coronal densities is straightforward *provided* we have made a suitable assumption about the three-dimensional structure of the corona. This assumption is necessary since we have observations in only two dimensions. Hence, strictly, we obtain only a coronal density distribution which reproduces the observations; this density distribution may not be unique. Usually one assumes spherical symmetry, and there seems little doubt that the large-scale density structure of the corona is known. Some typical results are shown in Table 2.1. At a given heliocentric distance, the density decreases (by a factor ≈ 2) as one goes from the equator to the pole.

Temperatures

The temperature of the corona can be shown in a variety of ways to be approximately 1 to 2×10^6 °K. The density gradients can be utilized with the hydrostatic equation to give the temperature required; this method gives approximately 1.5×10^6 °K, and this value is raised if refinements such as the coronal fine structure are included. The fact that the corona is expanding and hence not in hydrostatic equilibrium does not sensibly alter the temperature estimates in the main body of the corona for, say $r < 3\ R_\odot$, because the kinetic energy of the expansion per unit mass is quite small compared with the thermal and gravitational energies per unit mass. Thus, hydrostatic equilibrium is a good approximation sufficiently close to the Sun, even though the corona is not *strictly* in hydrostatic equilibrium. We know that the corona is expanding because of direct measurements of the outflowing plasma (proton-electron gas) on deep space probes such as Mariner II.

The radio brightness measurements give temperatures of approximately 1 million °K, although the results are fairly uncertain. The radio emission at, say, 18 mc/sec is thermal in origin and depends on the temperature. The trajectories (shown in Figure 2.13) are computed from Snell's law for refraction and a given density. The emergent emission from the corona is simply the emission at each point reduced by $e^{-\tau}$, where τ is the *intervening opacity*. Thus the transfer problem for radio waves can be considered in a manner analogous to Equation (2.10), but where the opacity is measured along the trajectory.

The temperature of the corona can also be determined by requiring that the highly ionized atoms observed through the coronal emission be produced and in the proper ratio. Ionization in the corona occurs by electron impact, and recombination occurs by electron capture. Since both processes are proportional to the electron density, this quantity cancels out in an equilibrium situation, and the ionization depends only on the temperature and the mechanism. For some years the ionization temperature, based on simple radiative recombination, was below 1×10^6 °K. However, it is now known that attention must be paid to possible intermediate steps in the recombination process, and a particular process called dielectronic recombination seems to be dominant. Calculations based on this latter process indicate an ionization temperature between 2 and 2.5×10^6 °K.

Finally, the temperatures can be determined directly from the observed widths of the coronal emission lines under the assumption that they are broadened by the thermal doppler effect alone. For this case, the line widths are proportional to $(T/\mu)^{1/2}$, where T is the temperature and μ is the atomic weight of the ion. Typical values for the quiet corona cluster near 2×10^6 °K.

In summary, the values for the temperature of the quiet corona are all consistent with a temperature of 2×10^6 °K.

Origin

For years many sources of energy for the maintenance of the corona have been proposed, including meteoritic infall from the interplanetary medium. It is now believed that the corona is heated solely by mechanical energy originating from the hydrogen convection zone, as discussed in Section 2.2. This energy is lost by conduction, outward into the interplanetary gas and inward into the chromosphere, and by radiation.

solar and
stellar
activity

3.1 INTRODUCTION

The general area of solar activity is one of the most interesting, most spectacular, and least understood branches of solar physics. The visual features of this "activity" are sunspots, faculae, prominences, flares, and active coronal regions; each of these are, of course, discussed in this chapter. However, most of these features are related to intense and localized magnetic fields in the Sun. These intense fields are thought to be related to or derived from the general solar magnetic field. Hence, the next section contains a discussion of the evidence for a general solar magnetic field. The treatment of solar activity concludes with the introduction of the concept of a *center of activity*, which serves as an idea around which to unify the multifarious facts which require assimilation. The chapter concludes with a review of our speculations and suspicions concerning stellar activity.

3.2 THE GENERAL SOLAR MAGNETIC FIELD

The existence of solar magnetic fields in sunspots has been known for decades; however, the measurement of the general field is a comparatively recent event because of the refined instruments required. The strength of the magnetic field is established from line splitting due to the Zeeman effect (see Section 3.3); sunspots have fields of hundreds of gauss, while the general solar field in the polar regions is on the order of 1 gauss.

The existence of the polar field is suggested by the form of the polar coronal rays. Nonetheless, the conclusive establishment of the field depends on its measurement. Figure 3.1 shows an early magnetograph of the Sun, which clearly shows the general field as well as some of the stronger magnetic regions. Such magnetograms are now considered to be routine. It is now known, for example, that the Sun's general or polar field reverses polarity with the same period (11 years) as the solar cycle (see Section 3.3).

The maintenance of the general solar field is a stimulating challenge to the theorist, which so far does not have a convincing answer. The two most popular theories are (1) The field is a natural result of the Sun's formation, i.e., a fossil. Calculations of the decay time for a magnetic field under idealized solar conditions indicate that this is not impossible. (2) The field is maintained from the sustaining fields generated by the dynamo action from motion of solar material across existing lines of force. Detailed calculations have not verified this approach, but attempts to disprove the dynamo have also failed. Neither of these theories accounts per se for the field reversal mentioned above, and we should consider that no working hypothesis concerning the origin and maintenance of the general solar field is available.

3.3 SUNSPOTS AND MAGNETIC REGIONS

Introduction and Description

Sunspots have been known for several hundred years and in appearance are composed of a dark center, called the umbra, and a less dark region, called the penumbra (Figure 3.2). Granulation has been found in the otherwise structureless umbra, and the penumbra is found to be an assemblage of filaments oriented radially with respect to the center of the umbra. Typical diameters of sunspots range from thousands to tens of thousands of kilometers. Large spot groups attain lengths of over 10^5 km. While there has been considerable debate through the years, it appears that sunspots are actually depressed areas on the solar surface.

Sunspots invariably occur in spot groups, which begin with a small spot or pore between the granules. Usually several nearby pores appear together, and a young spot group forms. The young group may disappear in an hour, or it may develop into a large group.

As almost everyone knows, the number of sunspots on the solar surface changes with time. This variation can be expressed quantitatively in terms of the Wolf relative sunspot number,

$$R = k \, (10g + f) \tag{3.1}$$

where f = number of individual sunspots
g = number of groups
k = a constant assigned to an individual observer and his equipment

Since the Sun rotates with a 27-day period which introduces an obvious change in R, averages taken over at least a 27-day time interval are almost universally used. Values of R are known with accuracy from 1700 A.D. to the present.

A plot of the yearly, average values of R shows that it varies periodically between $R > 100$ (sunspot maximum) and $R < 10$ (sunspot minimum). The average period from maximum to maximum is 11.2 years; however, it is 6.7 years from maximum to minimum, and 4.6 years from minimum to maximum.

The location of the sunspots on the solar disk also varies with time. The first spots of a cycle appear at $\pm 30°$ solar latitude, reach $\pm 15°$ by sunspot maximum, and appear at latitudes less than $\pm 10°$ by sunspot minimum. This migration of the sunspot zone is clearly shown in Figure 3.3, the butterfly diagram. We emphasize that only the region of appearance of the spots migrates; individual spots show little motion in their 1- or 2-month lifetime.

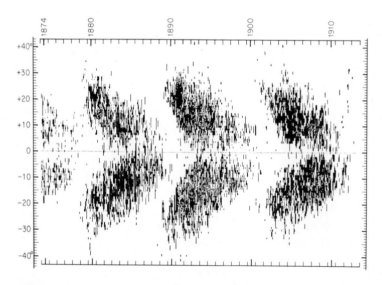

FIGURE 3.3   The Maunder butterfly diagram, showing the distribution of spot centers in heliographic latitude. *By permission from E. W. Maunder, Monthly Notices of the Royal Astronomical Society.*

Sunspots are regions with magnetic fields of hundreds and even thousands of gauss. This was discovered in 1908 by G. E. Hale, using the Zeeman effect. Simply, an observer looking along the magnetic field sees an ordinary line split into two Zeeman components by an amount which is directly proportional to the field strength (and constants of the atom). Solar observers use neutral iron lines in the red, where typical separations of 0.1 Å are found.

From detailed observations a picture of the magnetic field in sunspots can be built up. The distribution of field in a spot can be written approximately as

$$B\,(\rho) = B_m \left(1 - \frac{\rho^2}{b^2}\right) \tag{3.2}$$

where B_m = field at the center
       ρ = distance from the center
       b = value of ρ for the outer edge of the penumbra
The field is oriented vertically in the center of the spot and becomes progressively more horizontal as one moves away from the center and into the penumbra.

Intensities are also available for sunspots. The observations referring to the integrated spectrum for the center of the umbra give $I_{spot}/I_{phot} = 0.4$. Since the integrated emission is proportional to T^4, we may calculate the temperature of a sunspot by multiplying the solar effective temperature by $(0.4)^{1/4}$. This gives 4600°K, a temperature which is consistent with the appearance of the sunspot spectrum (including molecular bands). In fact, the general properties of the radiation emerging from sunspots is consistent with their being in radiative equilibrium—i.e., energy transport occurring (almost) entirely by radiation. Hence, it is convenient to think of sunspots as simply cooler regions of the photosphere; this coolness can be understood in terms of the fact that the strong magnetic field associated with sunspots inhibits the convective transport of energy in the upper part of the hydrogen convection zone. Thus, if the field is strong enough, less energy is supplied to the bottom of the photosphere, and the region which we call a sunspot appears cooler.

Motions in sunspots, called the Evershed effect, are also known; the velocities involved as ≈ 2 km/sec. A flow into the spot is found for strong lines (hence high in the atmosphere) and an outflow is found for weak lines (low in the atmosphere). These motions are poorly understood.

Spot Groups and Magnetic Regions

We have noted that sunspots almost invariably occur in groups which can be assigned to three main classes: (1) Unipolar groups, α. These are single spots or a spot group with the same magnetic polarity. (2) Bipolar groups, β. Here the preceding (p) and following (f) spots, taken in the sense of the solar rotation, are of opposite magnetic polarity. (3) Complex groups, γ. These have many spots of both polarities but cannot reasonably be classified as β groups. Some 90 percent of the groups are β, 10 percent are α, and less than 1 percent are γ.

A very interesting fact arises in the problem of the missing spots. Often the distribution of faculae (see Section 3.4) around an α group resembles the distribution of faculae around a β group. When this occurs, a magnetic region is found in the position of the missing spot. This situation serves to emphasize the fact that sunspots are apparently only a by-product of more basic processes responsible for solar activity, namely, the magnetic region. These regions are directly related to the sunspots and, of course, contain them. However, the sunspots constitute only a part of the magnetic regions (as in the case of our "missing spot"), and it is clearly desirable to work in terms of the *total magnetic region*. In Section 3.7, we have occasion to mention the unipolar magnetic regions (UMRs), or areas of one magnetic polarity, which are analogous to the unipolar spot groups.

Hence, we formulate the so-called sunspot laws of polarity in terms of the bipolar magnetic region (BMR). These are (1) The p and f portions (preceding and following portions, as explained above) of the BMR are of opposite polarity; (2) the p portions are of opposite polarity in the northern and southern hemispheres;

(3) the p part of the BMR in each hemisphere changes polarity with each new solar cycle. Since we know that the general field also reverses polarity with each new cycle, the true length of the field solar cycle is some 22 years. We also note that the magnetic flux ($= \int B dA$, where B is the field and A is the area) is equal in the p and f portions of the BMR.

Much of the preceding discussion is consistent with a mechanism for solar activity based on the occasional emergence of a loop of the general, subphotospheric, magnetic field into the visible portion of the solar atmosphere. The general idea is shown in Figure 3.4. On this model, due to H. W. Babcock, the general field is drawn into the east-west configuration shown by the solar differential rotation. The general scheme shown in Figure 3.4 naturally satisfies the polarity laws for hemispheres and p and f portions of

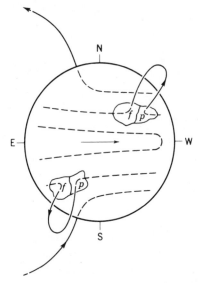

FIGURE 3.4   Schematic illustration of Babcock's mechanism for the production of sunspots. *By permission from H. W. Babcock, The Astrophysical Journal, published by the University of Chicago Press. Copyright, 1961, by the University of Chicago.*

the BMR. The model can account for other properties of BMRs, but it is considered far from final; it undoubtedly will have to be modified as more evidence is gathered.

3.4 FACULAE

Terminology

Bright regions seen near the solar limb in integrated light are called photospheric faculae or faculae. Bright regions found on K-line or Hα spectroheliograms are called chromospheric faculae or *plages faculaires* (French), which is usually shortened to *plages*. Such features are quite clearly shown in Figure 2.11. In this section, we refer to the single physical entity and its manifestations as a facula.

Properties

Faculae are distributed in solar latitude roughly the same way as sunspots. This is expected because sunspots are invariably accompanied by faculae; note, however, that faculae need not be accompanied by sunspots (for example, recall the case of the "missing sunspots" discussed in the last section). Faculae also precede the sunspots in time and outlast them by several solar rotations.

Faculae are observable in white light only near the limb of the Sun and not near the center of the disk. The limb observations mean that they are brighter and hence hotter than their surroundings high in the solar atmosphere. They must be cooler in the lower regions than their surroundings to be invisible near the center of the disk. Hence, faculae are obviously not in radiative equilibrium, and the question of an additional energy source is immediately raised.

Faculae seem to exhibit basically the same fine structure as the quiet chromosphere, viz., the granules, the coarse mottles, and the network. Thus, the faculae could be basically the same as the quiet chromosphere but with a much higher density of the bright granules or mottles. The way a facular region disperses seems to support this view. A facular region never disappears suddenly; it always merges smoothly into the chromospheric network.

Theory of Faculae

Faculae apparently arise from an intensification of the process which normally heats the chromosphere. Faculae are also known to have a remarkable, detailed correspondence with magnetic regions with fields greater than 20 gauss. Since we also know that mechanical energy is (produced and) deposited with greater efficiency in regions with magnetic fields, we obtain a qualitative theory of faculae by noting that the emergence of a BMR supplies the requisite magnetic field.

This picture also allows a qualitative understanding of the scale of the chromospheric network. Recent observations have discovered photospheric motions resembling granulation, but on a much larger scale, and hence, called the supergranulation. The diameter of the supergranulation is close to the meshwidth of the granulation. For the material involved, any magnetic field is effectively frozen into the material. Thus, if the supergranulation is a large convective cell, the magnetic field is preferentially convected to the cell boundary, where the field strength should be enhanced. This in turn increases the mechanical energy deposition, and the chromospheric network could result.

3.5 FLARES

Observational Facts

Flares are localized short-lived bursts of light occurring in the vicinity of sunspots. They are sometimes seen in integrated (white) light, but they are best and most frequently observed in Hα (the $n = 3$ to $n = 2$ transition in the Balmer series, λ6,563). Flares are of interest as a problem in solar physics, but they are also important because of their terrestrial effects, such as aurorae and the interruption of radio communication.

A classification system based on area and brightness is available; in increasing order of "importance," we have microflares, subflares (1^-), 1, 2, 3, and 3^+. The latter two classes are largely responsible for terrestrial effects. The light curve for flares shows a rapid rise to peak intensity, a short stay at maximum intensity, and a slow return to the preflare level. The curves are of similar shape for flares of different importances, but the time scales differ. An Imp. 1 flare lasts some 20 min, while an Imp. 3^+ flare lasts 3 hrs. The visual spectrum of a flare is not greatly different from the flash spectrum.

Flares are quite frequent on the Sun during solar maximum. The daily rate for flares of Imp. $\geqslant 1$ is approximately $R/25$. Thus at sunspot maximum, $R \approx 100$ and we have a flare every 6 hrs.

Figure 3.5 shows the development of a flare. Notice particularly the fine structure. Flares often brighten up or enhance portions of the facular network successively. Perhaps even more important is the fact that the chromospheric fine structure is left unchanged. A typical flare area is $\sim 10^{19}$ cm^2. Considerable mass motions are known to occur in connection with flares.

Finally, it is known that flares occur mostly near complex or γ groups usually when a change in the group structure is occurring.

Theory of Flares

The total rate of energy output from a flare has been estimated at 10^{28} ergs/sec; flares typically last some 10^3 sec for a total output of 10^{31} ergs. If this energy comes from a region with an area of 10^{19} cm^2 and a thickness of 10^8 cm, then the energy requirement is 10^4 ergs/cm^3. Such energies are not available from thermal sources or mass motions. The energy contained in the magnetic field is simply $B^2/8\pi$ (ergs/cm^3), and fairly reasonable values for the chromosphere of about 1,000 gauss can satisfy the energy requirement.

One conceptual point must be made before proceeding. The flare is by definition something we observe. There is thus a strong possibility of the confusion of cause and effect. The visual flare may be only one indication of some flare event which we do not see directly. There is considerable evidence for this event, since flares also produce mass motions and energetic cosmic ray particles which we observe at the Earth. Hence, in recent years it has been profitable to think in terms of a flare event which produces particles of high energy. Some of these leave the Sun and produce the effects observed at the Earth. The others interact with the chromospheric material to produce the observed radiation, the visible flare.

Thus, we need only account for the primary flare event. As we have mentioned before, magnetic energy seems to be the only source of energy available, and indeed, several flare models based on the annihilation of the magnetic field with subsequent release of energy are available. The details of these theories are yet to come.

3.6 PROMINENCES

Description

Prominences are observed in two contrasting situations, as shown in Figure 3.6. When seen at the limb, prominences show as arch-like structures resting on the chromosphere. When seen projected against the solar disk, they appear as dark filaments. The correspondence between prominences and filaments is clearly shown in Figure 3.6. Prominences project upward into the corona and can be regarded as dense regions in the corona. Temperatures of about 10,000°K are found for prominences. This temperature is about two orders of magnitude lower than the corona, while the densities are about two orders of magnitude higher. Thus, approximate pressure equilibrium exists between the prominences and the corona. Magnetic fields are obviously quite important in the study of prominences, as we shall see.

There are basically two types of prominences: (1) the sunspot prominences and (2) the quiescent prominences. The sunspot prominences are found in spot groups in the first week of their existence. They appear as loops rooted in the spot group or as condensations at a roughly constant height. Typical heights for these structures range from 50,000 to 100,000 km.

The quiescent prominences either are not associated with sunspots (but with faculae) or do not appear until 1 month (or one solar rotation) after the first spots. This is the type of prominence shown in Figure 3.6.

A development quiescent prominence has a thickness of 8,000 km, a height of 50,000 km, and a length of about 200,000 km. The solar differential rotation causes prominences to lengthen and tends to make them lie east-west.

While the large-scale structure of prominences is rather constant, considerable motions (mostly downward) are found in the fine structure. Ocassionally, the large-scale structure of the prominence undergoes rapid change. The prominence can flow into the chromosphere, or it can be hurled into space. These sudden disappearances take only a few hours, and a new similar prominence usually appears in the same place after a few days.

Theory of Prominences

Two points require explanation: (1) What keeps the prominence from being dissipated by the corona? (2) What holds the prominences up?

If we grant ourselves the luxury of assuming an initial perturbation to produce a fledgling prominence, we then seek a mechanism to maintain it. Since the prominence is probably composed of condensed coronal material, it naturally receives with each particle the energy corresponding to its origin in a 2×10^6 °K corona. The problem is then to radiate away this energy at a sufficiently fast rate; Lyman continuum radiation ($\lambda < 912$ Å, caused by recombinations directly to the $n = 1$ state in neutral hydrogen) seems capable of meeting this requirement for prominences of typical dimensions.

The problem of support does not directly relate to the sunspot prominences which last only a few days. Here the rate of condensation is apparently balanced by the rate at which the material slides down the magnetic field lines into the chromosphere.

However, the quiescent prominences often last for several solar

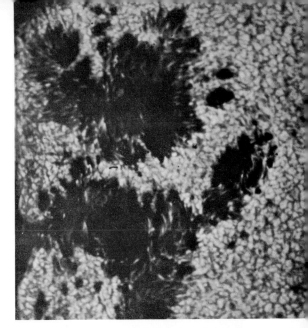

FIGURE 3.2 Balloon photograph of sunspots clearly showing the features described in the text. By permission from Project Stratoscope of Princeton University, sponsored by the Office of Naval Research, the National Science Foundation, and the National Aeronautics and Space Administration.

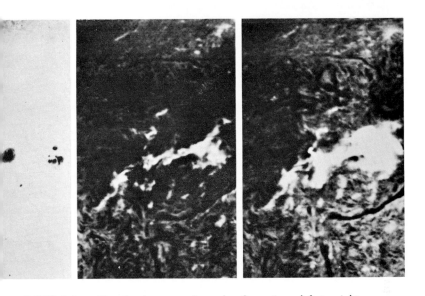

FIGURE 3.5 The development of a solar flare. From left to right: a white-light photograph of the spot group; the flare in Hα 11 min later; the flare in Hα 22 min later. Notice the fine structure. (Mount Wilson and Palomar Observatories). From "Science in Space" by L. V. Berkner and H. Odishaw. Copyright 1961. McGraw-Hill Book Company. Used by permission.

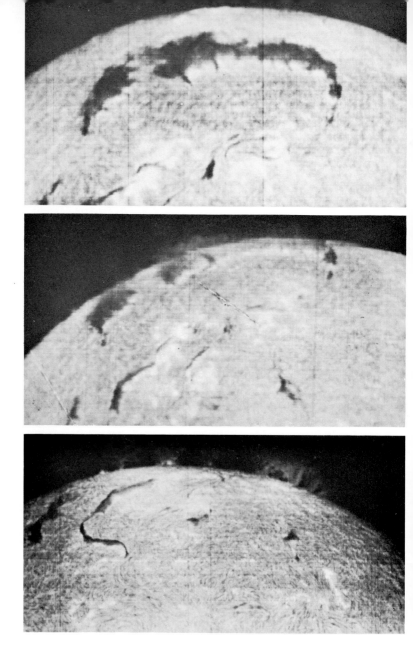

FIGURE 3.6   Photographic sequence illustrating the correspondence between filaments and prominences. From top to bottom, the photographs were taken on February 2, 3, and 5, 1959, respectively. By permission from the Observatoire de Paris-Meudon.

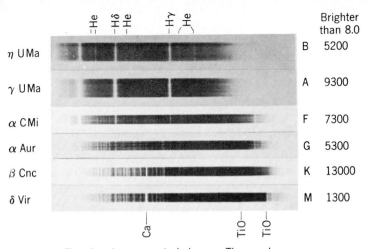

The six primary spectral classes. The number
of stars brighter than the eight magnitude in
each class is shown on the right.

FIGURE 5.6   The six primary spectral classes. The number of stars
brighter than the eighth magnitude in each class is shown on the right.
Yerkes Observatory photograph.

Luminosity effects at A0

The H lines become progressively stronger
on passing from the supergiant HR 1040
to the main-sequence star α Lyrae

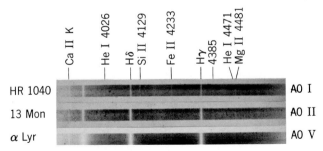

At A0 He I 4026 is faint or absent, and is
weaker than Si II 4129. The lines of Fe II
are strengthened in the supergiants.

FIGURE 5.7   Luminosity effects at A0 as described in the text. Yerkes
Observatory photograph.

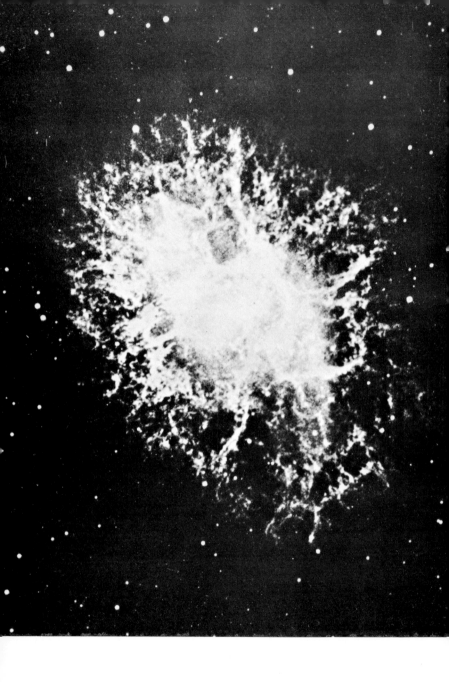

FIGURE 7.1   200″ photograph of the Crab nebulae in red light. By permission from the Mt. Wilson and Palomar Observatories.

rotations. The locations of filaments are found to be regions where the magnetic field is parallel to the solar surface; this is easy to imagine for the case of a filament straddling a BMR. Thus the prominences can be supported by the magnetic field, since the field inhibits motions perpendicular to itself. If the magnetic field undergoes rapid changes, then the corresponding rapid changes in prominences (such as sudden disappearances) can be qualitatively understood.

3.7 CORONAL REGIONS

There are three distinct types of active regions in the corona. The patches observable in the coronal green line and showing the yellow line are called permanent coronal condensations. These areas generally follow the facular area in brightness, and they have higher temperatures and densities than the undisturbed corona.

The so-called sporadic coronal condensations are thought to be objects with temperatures lower than permanent coronal condensations. The former show the green line, red line, and Hα ($\lambda6,563$ of neutral hydrogen).

Finally, there are the coronal C regions, with an enhanced green line but no yellow line. Historically, these regions were called M regions from geophysical evidence. The great terrestrial magnetic storms are correlated with flares, but the lesser magnetic storms also show a 27-day period; thus the M regions were the postulated origin of the geophysical disturbance. In recent years, the C and M regions have been assumed identical. They may correspond to UMRs and possibly even to the long coronal streamers often seen on eclipse photographs. The situation regarding the various cross identifications should not be considered as final.

The general form of the corona undergoes a variation which is directly related to the solar cycle; this variation is described in Section 2.3.

As we have indicated in the last few sections, there is a myriad of phenomena comprising solar activity. This complexity has led to the concept of a center of activity (CA). In Table 3.1 we summarize the properties of a fully developed, typical CA. We emphasize that the history of an individual CA may differ considerably from the representative account given.

In reviewing the phenomena listed in Table 3.1 and the explanations given in preceding sections of this chapter, one is struck by the preeminent importance of the magnetic field. Hence, one is pushed to the hypothesis that all manifestations of solar activity are due to the emergence (from subphotospheric layers) and subsequent evolution of a magnetic region.

TABLE 3.1   LIFE HISTORY OF TYPICAL CENTER OF ACTIVITY*

DAY	SPOTS	MAGNETIC REGION	FACULAE
1	Spots may originate a few hours after faculae appear, but usually only pores.	Assumes bipolar character.	Systematic alignment of chromospheric fine structure around area which becomes bright facular speck. Speck develops east-west orientation.
2	West end of facular regions shows first *p* spot.	Characteristic dimension magnetic region ⌐ 50,000 km.	Area increases in size and brightness.
5	*f* spot appears at east end of faculae; other small spots in between; main spots are continually separating.		
11	Maximum development.	Field irregular and variable.	Size and brightness increases; dimensions ⌐10^5 km.

If we consider some general properties of stellar activity based on analogy with solar activity, we are faced with an almost insurmountable task.

However, some consideration of the general properties of the observations available is advisable. Our fund of knowledge is based primarily on optical observations of brightness changes and to a lesser extent on observations obtained with standard spectroscopic techniques. If we take the general view that all phenomena related to the emergence of subphotospheric fields are "stellar activity," it is clear that many phenomena will remain unexplored; however, two general types of phenomena are known which could be stellar activity.

FLARES	PROMINENCES (Filaments)	CORONAL REGIONS
		Green patch forms after spots appear. Parallels facular development. Same extent as facular region.
First signs of activity.	Small, unstable filaments appear around faculae.	Green line increases.
Flares between f and p spots.	Sunspot prominences appear.	
Peak of flare activity.		Yellow-line brightness with flare activity.

TABLE 3.1   Continued

DAY	SPOTS	MAGNETIC REGION	FACULAE
27	Usually only p spot remains; the f spot disappears by being "bridged" by bright, normal photosphere.	Magnetic flux reaches maximum.	Facular area still increases in size.
54	No spots.		Brightness decreases and area cut in half by filament.
81		Field strength declines.	Area constant, dissolves into bright facular network (still brighter than normal chromosphere).
108			Faculae dissolved.
135		Area occupies one-twentieth of disk.	CA undetectable in photosphere or chromosphere except for some fine structure oriented around filament.
162–270		BMR fills one-fifth of disk and changes into UMR.	

* Note: East and west are as the Sun is seen from the Earth.

First, there are the magnetic variables. The same general techniques based on the Zeeman effect used to study solar magnetic fields have been applied to other stars by H. W. Babcock. The problem is made more complex by the observation of the entire stellar disk at once; hence, any magnetic field obtained is a crude average over the disk. However, certain A-type stars (see Chapter 5) show integrated fields of up to some kilogauss which reverse polarity with periods of a few days. Some absorption lines of the rare earth elements undergo changes with the same period. The

FLARES	PROMINENCES (Filaments)	CORONAL REGIONS
Flares rare.	Stable filament forms on poleward side of facular area, makes angle of some 40° with meridian and points toward p spot.	Maximum green-line brightness.
	Filament now $\sim 10^5$ km in length and starting to swing toward east-west orientation.	Green line decreases in brightness.
	Length increases and orientation continues toward east-west.	
	Maximum length achieved and nearly east-west (parallel to equator).	
	Length decreases; prominence starts poleward migration.	
	Filament changes structure and joins polar crown filaments.	Coronal streamers, associated with UMR.

oblique rotator hypothesis attributes this behavior to "spots" which are brought into view by the rotation of the star about its axis. If the star had immense sunspots or very bright faculae, the observations could be satisfied.

The second type of stellar activity is apparently related to flare-like occurrences. A variety of such activity observed in dwarf M stars seems most directly related to solar flares. These stars show bright outbursts which increase their total brightness by one or more magnitudes and which last for times of a few minutes to a half hour. It must be fully appreciated that spectra of such events are difficult to obtain; luckily, a spectrogram of a flare of UV Ceti has been obtained by A. H. Joy. This spectrogram shows a continuum, bright, wide (≈ 2 Å) lines of hydrogen, bright lines of He I, and $\lambda 4,686$ of He II. This description is not unlike the description of the spectrum of a solar flare. The brightness increase is comparable to that of a large solar flare.

Since flares (of the same size) become increasingly easier to detect as one goes to stars of lower effective temperature, our knowledge of solar and dwarf M stars suggests that flares may be a common occurrence in late type stars. They may be important in many types of stars and may also contribute significantly to the loss of mass from stars.

solar and stellar interiors

The interior of stars in large part consists of highly ionized material at high temperatures. Since the vast majority of stars are thought to be stable and in existence on long time scales, we naturally take them to be in hydrostatic equilibrium. These time scales for stars also dictate that the source of stellar energy is nuclear energy.

One must constantly bear in mind the fact that solar and stellar interiors are not generally accessible to observation. In the next section, we begin with the basic equations for solar interiors, and then in Section 4.2 we discuss the solar model. Subsequent sections discuss stellar interiors from the viewpoint of the results and how the basic equations (valid for solar interiors) must be modified to obtain them.

4.1 BASIC EQUATIONS

The equations given in this section are the basis of the study of stellar interiors and are generally valid for all stars. However, the exact forms for some of the equations given in this section are applicable strictly to stars similar to the Sun.

Hydrostatic Equilibrium

For a nonrotating, nonvariable star, the assumption of hydrostatic equilibrium immediately gives

$$\frac{dP}{dr} = \rho \, \frac{GM(r)}{r^2} \tag{4.1}$$

where r = distance from the center of the star
  P = pressure
  ρ = density
  G = constant of gravitation
  $M(r)$ = mass contained within the spherical shell of radius r
Equation (4.1) states that the gravitational force on a given volume element is balanced by the pressure difference.

The mass in any spherical shell is simply $4\pi\rho r^2\,dr$, and hence, the rate of change of $M(r)$ with r is

$$\frac{dM(r)}{dr} = 4\pi\rho r^2 \tag{4.2}$$

This is the mass equation.

Energy-balance Equation

In a manner analogous to the mass equation, the energy-balance equation can be derived and is

$$\frac{dL(r)}{dr} = 4\pi\rho r^2\varepsilon \tag{4.3}$$

Here $L(r)$ is the total luminosity from the layers below r in ergs per second, and ε is the rate of energy generation in ergs per gram-second.

Energy Transport

Conductive transport is thought to be unimportant in stellar interiors (except for white dwarfs and the cores of red giants), and hence we consider transport by radiation and by convection.

In stellar interiors, the radiation field is nearly isotropic, and the radiative transport in terms of the temperature reduces to

$$\left(\frac{dT}{dr}\right)_{\text{rad}} = \frac{3K\rho L(r)}{4\sigma c\,T^3 4\pi r^2} \tag{4.4}$$

where $T = $ temperature
$\quad\quad K = $ opacity (which must be suitably defined
$\quad\quad\quad\quad$ in terms of the average overall frequencies)
$\quad\quad \sigma = $ Stefan-Boltzmann constant
$\quad\quad c = $ velocity of light

If the transport of energy is by convection, Equation (4.4) does not apply. The tendency of convective transport is to reduce the temperature gradient to the adiabatic value of the temperature gradient. This process is very effective in stellar interiors—so efficient that the adiabatic gradient is a good approximation to the temperature gradient for layers in convective equilibrium. Thus, we have

$$\left(\frac{dT}{dr}\right)_{ad} = \frac{dP}{dr}\frac{T}{P}\left(1 - \frac{1}{\gamma}\right)$$ (4.5)

where γ is the ratio of the specific heat at constant pressure to the specific heat at constant volume ($\gamma = 5/3$ for an ionized gas). Equation (4.5) follows directly from the adiabatic condition, $\rho = \text{const } P^{1/\gamma}$, when the perfect-gas law [Equation (4.6)] and logarithmic differentiation are used.

When constructing a stellar model, one must test the temperature gradient at each point to see if the Schwarzschild instability criterion [Equation (2.18)] applies; this determines whether Equation (4.4) or (4.5) is used to describe the energy transport.

Equation of State

The equation of state for stellar interiors is the perfect-gas equation,

$$P = \frac{k\rho T}{\mu m_{\text{H}}} = NkT$$ (4.6)

where N = particle density
μ = mean molecular weight
m_{H} = mass of the hydrogen atom
$(= 1.67 \times 10^{-24} \text{ g})$
k = Boltzmann constant $(= 1.38 \times 10^{-16} \text{ erg/deg})$

This equation is valid for a wide range of normal stellar conditions.

The mean molecular weight must be determined before this equation can be used, and this implies knowledge of ionization conditions in stellar interiors. Hydrogen and helium are entirely ionized, and calculations with the Saha equation [Equation (5.17)] show that the heavier elements are almost entirely ionized.

If A is the atomic weight of the heavy nucleus, the results can be
represented by approximately $A/2$ free particles per atom. Now
let X, Y, and Z be the fraction of the mass of hydrogen, helium,
and heavy elements (or metals), respectively. (Note: $X + Y + Z$
$= 1$.) Thus, the number of particles per unit volume is simply
the sum of the number of particles per atom times the mass fraction times ρ/m_H, divided by the atomic weight of the species.
Thus, for hydrogen, we have $2X\rho/m_H$; for helium, $\frac{3}{4} Y\rho/m_H$; and
for the metals, $(A/2) Z/Am_H = Z\rho/2m_H$. These expressions can
be compared with the definition of the mean molecular weight
[Equation (4.6)] to yield

$$\mu = \frac{1}{2X + \dfrac{3}{4} Y + \dfrac{1}{2} Z} \qquad (4.7)$$

Since we consider that the stellar composition is given from
photospheric studies, the mean molecular weight can be computed
and the specification of Equation (4.6) is complete.

The Opacity

Possible sources of opacity in stellar interiors are bound-free
transitions, free-free transitions (bremsstrahlung), and Thomson
scattering by free electrons. The dominant process in the solar
interior is bound-free transition of heavy elements. To accurately
determine the opacity as a function of frequency is a difficult task,
since it requires the specification of the abundance and stage of
ionization of many elements. This calculation is best performed
numerically.

However, we require a mean opacity integrated over frequency.
Since the major portion of the energy transport occurs where the
opacity is small, the final K is an *inverse mean* of K_ν with a
weighting function dictated by the form of Equation (4.4); a K
thus formed is called the Rosseland mean-absorption coefficient.
The approximation for the bound-free opacity used in the Sun is
called the Kramer's opacity or Kramer's law.

There are two sequences of nuclear-reaction rates which are of great importance in stellar interiors. The first sequence is the carbon cycle, suggested by H. Bethe. The reactions are

$$C^{12} + H^1 \to N^{13} + \gamma$$
$$N^{13} \to C^{13} + e^+ + \text{neutrino}$$
$$C^{13} + H^1 \to N^{14} + \gamma$$
$$N^{14} + H^1 \to O^{15} + \gamma \quad \text{(4.8)}$$
$$O^{15} \to N^{15} + e^+ + \text{neutrino}$$
$$N^{15} + H^1 \to C^{12} + He^4$$

The notation here is standard, with the atomic weight shown as a superscript; γ is a gamma ray, and e^+ is a positron. The net effect in this sequence is to change $4H^1$ into 1 He^4 with C^{12} acting as a catalyst. This cycle liberates 4×10^{-5} erg per helium atom formed, an estimate which includes the energy loss through neutrinos.

The other process is the proton-proton cycle, given by

$$H^1 + H^1 \to D^2 + e^+ + \text{neutrino}$$
$$D^2 + H^1 \to He^3 + \gamma \quad \text{(4.9)}$$
$$He^3 + He^3 \to He^4 + H^1 + H^1$$

where D stands for the nucleus of deuterium, heavy hydrogen. The last line is the method usually assumed for completion of the proton-proton cycle; two other completions are possible, however. The total energy available in making one helium atom is 4.3×10^{-5} erg. The neutrino loss relative to this figure for the method of completion shown in Equation (4.9) is some 2 percent. The other methods of completion have neutrino losses of 4 percent and 29 percent. Thus, the completion route makes some quantitative difference.

The dependence of the various nuclear reaction rates on temperature is rather complicated, but since energy generation usually takes place in a fairly restricted region (temperature-wise), interpolation formulas can be used without serious loss of accuracy.

The interpolation formulas for the proton-proton cycle and the carbon cycle can be written as

$$\rho \varepsilon_{pp} = \varepsilon_1 \, \rho^2 \, X^2 \left(\frac{T}{10^6} \right)^\nu \qquad \text{(4.10)}$$

and

$$\rho \varepsilon_{cc} = \varepsilon_1 \, \rho^2 \, X X_{CN} \left(\frac{T}{10^6} \right)^\nu \qquad \text{(4.11)}$$

where $\rho \varepsilon_{pp}$ and $\rho \varepsilon_{cc}$ = energy generation rates, ergs/cm³-sec

ε_1 and ν = parameters in the interpolation formulas (known from tables)

X_{CN} = total mass fraction of all carbons and nitrogens together ($X_{CN} \approx Z/3$)

The temperature dependences for these two cycles are quite different. For temperatures of 10 million °K the proton-proton chain is completely dominant, and ν lies between 4.5 and 5. At 30 million °K the carbon cycle dominates and ν is between 15 and 16. The general behavior is shown in Figure 4.1.

Neutrino Astronomy

We noted at the beginning of this chapter that stellar interiors are generally inaccessible to observation. This situation may be changed in the not too distant future with the advent of neutrino astronomy. Neutrinos arise only in the energy-producing regions of stars, and since their cross section for reaction is virtually nil, they leave the star unhindered.

Because of their small cross section, the detection of neutrinos is an extremely difficult task—one which seems possible, however. This information gained from neutrinos could provide valuable information, useful in many ways. For example, the energies ($\sim$ Mev) of the neutrinos involved in the different ways of completing the proton-proton chain are different and could be measured.

4.2 SOLAR MODELS

The problem of constructing a model from the equations given in Section 4.1 is a formidable one. Historically, analytic techniques

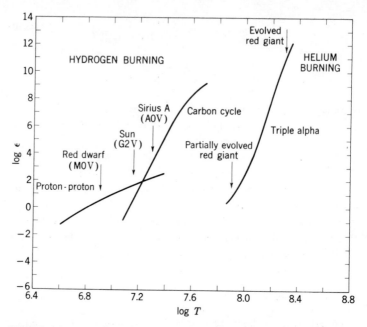

FIGURE 4.1   Nuclear energy generation rates as a function of tempera-ture for typical stellar conditions. Various stars are marked at the position of their central temperatures. *After M. Schwarzschild.*

have been pushed to their limit to achieve a qualitative under-standing of stellar models. However, detailed models require numerical techniques.

The problem is one of seven equations in seven unknowns. The variables are P, ρ, $M(r)$, ε, $L(r)$, T, and K; the equations are (1) hydrostatic equilibrium, (2) mass, (3) energy balance, (4) en-ergy transport, (5) perfect-gas law (equation of state), (6) opacity tables, and (7) the rates of nuclear-energy generation. Thus, the problem is solvable when the composition (X, Y, and Z) is speci-fied and when the boundary conditions are given. The boundary is, of course, the solar atmosphere, discussed in Chapter 2. In addition, the star must have the proper mass, luminosity, and radius.

One problem concerning the details of the solution deserves further mention; namely, it is not possible to start a solution at the surface or the center of the star and continue the solution through-out the star. The solutions starting from the center diverge near the surface, and the surface solutions diverge near the center. This difficulty is overcome by starting two solutions, an *interior* (or core) and an *envelope,* and fitting them together at a convenient interface. The process of joining the two solutions together is done by trial and error and greatly increases the labor involved in the construction of stellar models.

At best, however, this gives a model for the *initial Sun,* i.e., the Sun before nuclear reactions and evolution began. Estimates of the age of the Sun are based on the geophysical evidence giving the age of the solidification of the Earth's crust at 4.5 billion years. Thus, the computation of a model of the "present" Sun involves computing an initial Sun and letting it evolve for 4.5×10^9 years (see Section 6.1). If it resembles the Sun we know from the observations, the operation is considered a success.

A model for the present Sun due to R. Weymann is shown in Figures 4.2 and 4.3. The central depletion of hydrogen expected from the nuclear reactions is clearly shown. The proton-proton chain provides the main portion of the nuclear energy, although the carbon cycle may make a minor contribution. Finally, the deep interior of the Sun is in radiative equilibrium, but the region from $r/R_\odot = 0.86$ to just below the photosphere is in convective equilibrium.

4.3 BASIC EQUATIONS FOR STELLAR MODELS

Basic Equations and Modifications

Here we consider the required modification of our basic equations for the discussion of stellar models. The equations of hydrostatic equilibrium, mass, and energy balance remain unaltered and need no further discussion. The equations for energy transport by radiation and convection are unaltered, but we must consider that conduction by degenerate electrons in the cores of red giants and in white dwarfs is very efficient. These points are discussed later in this chapter.

Except for the case of degenerate matter (see Figure 4.4) the

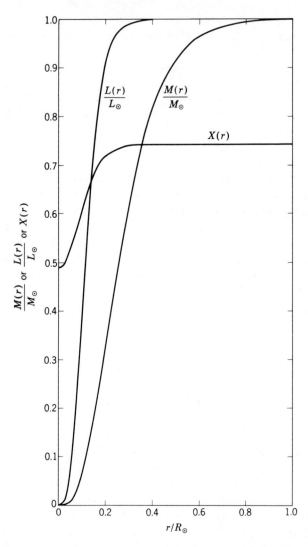

FIGURE 4.2   The run of luminosity, mass, and the fraction of hydrogen (X) on the basis of Weymann's model of the Sun. The central depletion of hydrogen is clearly shown. *From Solar System Astrophysics by J. C. Brandt and P. Hodge. Copyright, 1964. McGraw-Hill Book Company. Used by permission.*

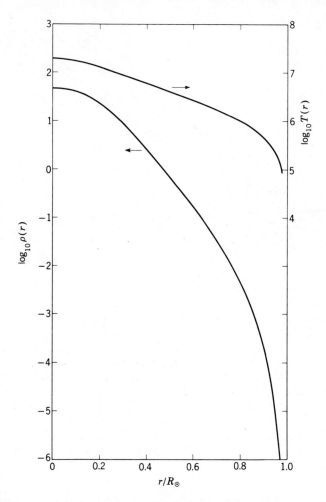

FIGURE 4.3 The run of temperature and density on the basis of Weymann's solar model. *From Solar System Astrophysics by J. C. Brandt and P. Hodge. Copyright, 1964. McGraw-Hill Book Company. Used by permission.*

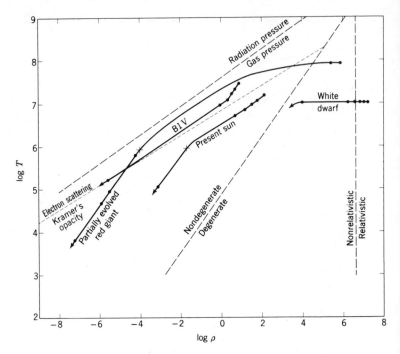

FIGURE 4.4.   A plot in the log ρ-log T plane showing the regions in which various equations of state and various opacities are valid. Each star is plotted as six dots which divide the star into five shells of approximately equal mass. The point on the right represents the center of the star; the left-hand point contains essentially all the mass but does not include the photospheric regions, which are in the direction indicated by the arrows. The cross on the solar curve marks the lower boundary of the hydrogen convection zone. *After M. Schwarzschild.*

equation of state requires only the addition of a term due to the radiation pressure, a function of temperature. This modification introduces no problem of principle and is important only in the central regions of massive stars.

Considerable information is shown in Figure 4.4 concerning the equation of state and the law of opacity. The heavy dashed lines show the lines of demarcation for the various equations of state; the light dashed line separates the region where the opacity is due to electron scattering (above) from the (lower) region where the

Kramer's opacity applies. Here we take Kramer's opacity to mean the bound-free absorptions by the heavier elements (as in the Sun) as well as free-free transitions of hydrogen and helium, since the latter are important in stars of low metal abundance. There is no concern about the opacity for the case of degenerate matter, since here the energy transport is by electron conduction.

The nuclear reaction rates given in Section 4.1 are, of course, still valid for the carbon cycle and the proton-proton chain. Hence, we need to consider when each of these cycles is dominant and when, if ever, other processes may be important in the energy generation. Figure 4.1 shows this information clearly and indicates that helium burning can occur if the temperature nears $10^8 °K$.

The triple-alpha scheme can be written as

$$He^4 + He^4 \rightarrow Be^8 + \gamma$$
$$Be^8 + He^4 \rightarrow C^{12} + \gamma \qquad \textbf{(4.12)}$$

This reaction converts three alpha particles into one carbon atom, with the resultant production of energy due to the mass defect. The energy-production rate $\varepsilon_{3\alpha}$ varies approximately at T^{+30} and is proportional to $\rho^2 Y^3$.

It is currently thought that additional reactions involving the heavy elements do not contribute appreciably to the rate of energy production, but they may be important in determining the relative abundances of the heavier elements.

Degenerate Matter in Stars

As we can see from Figure 4.4, large portions of white dwarfs and the cores of red giants are composed of degenerate matter. What is degenerate matter?

Physically, it is a limit on the density based on the Pauli exclusion principle; for densities less than the limit, matter can still obey Maxwell-Boltzmann statistics. Let us emphasize at the onset, that it is not the limit imposed by the possibility of the nuclei touching; the densities involved are still several orders of magnitude below this latter limit.

In most ordinary (low-density) applications, the distribution of momenta follows the Maxwell-Boltzmann law and hence obeys the perfect-gas law. The Pauli exclusion principle for electrons in atoms states that no two electrons in the same atom can exist in the same quantum state; i.e., their quantum numbers must differ at least in their spin. The exclusion principle for gases states that in each volume of the six-dimensional phase space ($dx\,dy\,dz\,dv_x\,dv_y\,dv_z$) of size h^3, we can have at most two electrons of opposite spin. Imagine that the total momentum p is a coordinate in a spherical coordinate system; then the exclusion principle demands

$$N(p)\,dp \leqslant \frac{2}{h^3}\,4\pi\,p^2\,dp \qquad (4.13)$$

where $N(p)\,dp$ is the number of electrons with momenta between p and $p + dp$. This should be compared with the corresponding expression for Maxwell-Boltzmann statistics, namely,

$$N(p)\,dp = \frac{N_e\,e^{-(p^2/2mkT)}}{(2\pi mkT)^{3/2}}\,4\pi p^2\,dp \qquad (4.14)$$

It is clear that these two distributions are not universally compatible, and this problem is shown in Figure 4.5. Equations (4.13) and (4.14) can be compared to ascertain the densities at which the effects of degeneracy are important.

Under stellar conditions, the usual gas laws apply up to densities of 10^2 to 10^3 g/cm^3, at which point the electrons begin to be degenerate. Densities of 10^5 to 10^6 g/cm^3 are required for the heavy particles to be degenerate, since they have larger volumes in phase space (because of their higher momentum for a given temperature). At densities of 10^6 g/cm^3 and above, large numbers of the electrons have relativistic energies, and they are said to be in the region of relativistic degeneracy.

A case of wide interest, because it is a good approximation in many cases, is the case of so-called *complete degeneracy*. Here, Equation (4.13) with the equal sign applies up to a cutoff momentum, p_0, and $N(p) = 0$ for $p > p_0$; this case is shown in

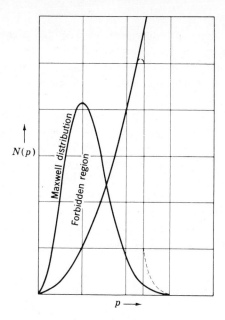

$N(p)$

Maxwell distribution

Forbidden region

$p \longrightarrow$

FIGURE 4.5   A diagram, due to S. Chandrasekhar, showing how the Maxwell distribution of momenta will violate the Pauli exclusion principle at high densities; see the text for discussion. *From Astrophysics by J. A. Hynek (ed.). Copyright, 1951. McGraw-Hill Book Company. Used by permission.*

Figure 4.5. For a completely degenerate-electron gas, the pressure for the nonrelativistic case is

$$P_e = \text{const} \times \rho^{5/3} \tag{4.15}$$

and for the relativistic case,

$$P_e = \text{const} \times \rho^{4/3} \tag{4.16}$$

The pressure due to atoms must also be computed and added to the electron pressure to give the total pressure. For most applications in stellar interiors, the atoms are not degenerate. Hence, when the electrons are degenerate, we add the normal gas pressure for the atoms to the degenerate-electron pressure to obtain the total pressure.

Energy transport in a degenerate-electron gas occurs by conduction. The process is analogous to conduction by electrons in a metal; in both cases, the electrons responsible for the energy transport are "free" in the sense that they do not belong to a specific atom or nucleus.

When the temperature and density are in the range where neither the completely degenerate- nor the perfect-gas equation of state applies, one is said to have *partial degeneracy*. The equation of state is known, and no difficulty of principle is encountered because of partial degeneracy.

This concludes our discussion of the alterations required of the basic equations under a variety of circumstances. Notice that we always have essentially seven equations in seven unknowns, and thus the problem is solvable in principle.

4.4 STELLAR STRUCTURE

Models which are considered reliable are available for most main-sequence stars, white dwarfs, and red giants. White dwarfs are characterized by high densities and degenerate matter. So-called main-sequence stars are the "normal" stars of astronomy, and the red giants are evolved main-sequence stars. These stars are further described in Chapters 5 and 6; see particularly Figure 5.1.

Mass Structure

The variation of the density ρ (with ρ_0 being the central density) given by a plot of ρ/ρ_0 as a function of radial distance r (in units of the star's radius R_*) serves as an indication of the mass structure of the stars; such a plot is shown in Figure 4.6. It is easily seen that the structure of white dwarfs and the structure of main-sequence stars from $0.6\,M_\odot$ to $10\,M_\odot$ (note: $M_\odot$ = the solar mass) are remarkably similar and fairly well represented by the *standard model* obtained by A. S. Eddington over 40 years ago. The standard model corresponds to a polytrope of index $n = 3$.

Polytropes are gases in which, for example, changes of pressure (P) and temperature (T) are related through $P^{(1-\gamma')}T^{\gamma'} = $ constant, where γ' is the *polytropic exponent;* for adiabatic changes

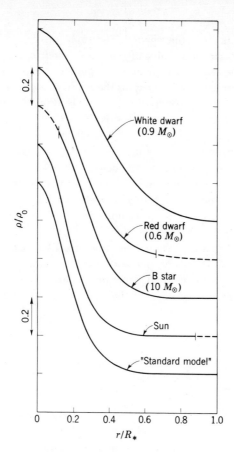

FIGURE 4.6   A comparison, as described in the text, of various "dwarf" models including the so-called *standard model*.

γ' is equal to the ratio of the specific heat at constant pressure to that at constant volume, i.e., $\gamma' = \gamma = c_p/c_v$. The *polytropic index* is the most convenient parameter and is defined by $n = (\gamma' - 1)^{-1}$. Thus for an adiabatic, highly ionized gas, $\gamma' = \gamma = 5/3$, and $n = 1.5$. The polytrope for $n = 3$ is a case of energy transport by radiation. Note that the polytropic equation is *not* an equation of state (which involves three variables: pressure, temperature, and density); the reduction of the number of variables is accomplished by specifying *how* the changes are to be made. This condition limits the range of validity of polytropic models, and while such simplifications are useful in early, exploratory investigations, they are no longer used extensively in the study of stellar models.

This situation of similarity (shown in Figure 4.6 for white dwarfs and main-sequence stars) does not hold for the red giants, as can be readily seen in Figure 4.7, which, we note, is a plot of $M(r)/M$ versus log ρ. Here it is seen that a red giant is composed of a dense core of degenerate helium with an outer convective envelope; the transition region between these extremes contains a shell source of energy produced by hydrogen burning. The key seems to be homogeneity in composition. Main-sequence stars and white dwarfs are the "before" and "after" for red giants, and they are homogeneous and similar in structure. Red giants are greatly dissimilar and completely inhomogeneous. Besides illustrating the great difference in internal structure, Figure 4.7 shows the large gamut of physics which must be understood to study stellar interiors.

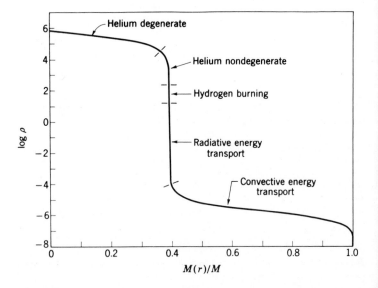

FIGURE 4.7   A model of a partially evolved red giant. *After M. Schwarzschild and H. Selberg.*

Considerable information concerning the physics and structure of stars is contained in Figures 4.1, 4.4, 4.6, and 4.7. These figures show the dominant physical processes in the various regions of stars as well as typical temperatures and densities for white dwarfs, red giants, and main-sequence stars.

We conclude with a word concerning the role of convection and its location. Figure 4.4 has the extent of the outer convective zone marked by a cross for the case of the Sun and the red giant. The central region of the B1 main-sequence star is also convective [out to about $M(r)/M = 0.2$], but it cannot be shown on the graph. The convective regions are also shown in Figure 4.6 as dashed lines.

Thus, early-type stars $(T_{eff} \approx 20,000°K)$ have convective cores which decrease in size as one goes to later-type stars. Around spectral-type F $(T_{eff} \approx 7500°K)$ an outer convective envelope begins to develop; the convective envelope deepens as one moves to later spectral types. This effect is shown in Figure 4.8, where two possible curves are shown; the uncertainty stems from our lack of knowledge of the *details* of how energy is carried by con-

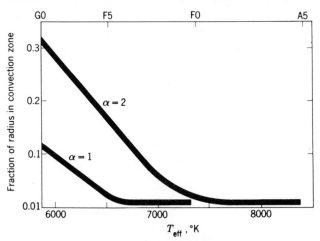

FIGURE 4.8   The depth of the hydrogen convection zone calculated under assumptions described in the text. *After N. Baker and R. Kippenhahn.*

vection. The working theory is based on the assumption that the convective bubbles (discussed in Chapter 2 in connection with the Schwarzschild stability criterion) travel one "mixing length" upward before they share their excess energy with their surroundings. The mixing-length theory itself has no way of determining the mixing length, but it is usually taken to be one or two scale heights (see Section 2.2); the curves marked $\alpha = 1$ and $\alpha = 2$ correspond to these two alternatives, respectively.

The Mass-Luminosity Relation

The observational basis for the mass-luminosity relation is discussed in Section 5.5. Here we give a simple discussion of the theoretical basis for it.

A characteristic density within a star is given simply by

$$\rho \propto \frac{M}{R^3} \tag{4.17}$$

The dependence of pressure on mass and radius can be obtained by inserting the last proportionality in the equation of hydrostatic equilibrium; when differentials are encountered, we adopt the following philosophy, as exemplified by our evaluation of dP/dr in the equation of hydrostatic equilibrium [Equation (4.1)]. The procedure is to substitute rough differences for the differential. Thus,

$$\frac{dP}{dr} \approx \frac{(P_c - P_s)}{R} \tag{4.18}$$

where P_c is the central pressure and P_s is the surface pressure. Since the surface pressure is small compared with any interior pressure, we set $P_s = 0$ and drop subscripts to obtain

$$\frac{dP}{dr} \propto \frac{P}{R} \tag{4.19}$$

This procedure is to be adopted in this discussion whenever differentials are encountered. Thus Equations (4.17), (4.19), and (4.1) give

$$P \propto \frac{M^2}{R^4} \tag{4.20}$$

Our functional dependences for pressure and density can be inserted into the perfect-gas law [Equation (4.6)] to obtain

$$T \propto \frac{M}{R}$$ (4.21)

Lastly, we substitute for density [from Equation (4.17)] and temperature [from Equation (4.21)] into the equation of radiative equilibrium [Equation (4.4)] to find

$$L \propto M^3$$ (4.22)

Notice that the radius cancels out in Equation (4.22). Despite the crude nature of our derivation, this dependence of L versus M gives a rough approximation to the observations which are discussed in Section 5.5. There the observed power dependence of L on M is shown to be between 2.8 and 4.0; these numbers bracket our crude value of 3.0.

The Voigt-Russell Theorem

This theorem states that if the pressure, the opacity, and the rate of energy generation are functions of the local values of the density, temperature, and the chemical composition only, then the structure of a star is uniquely determined by the mass and the chemical composition. We shall not prove this theorem; it is basically the statement of the mathematical completeness of our equations, which depend on an equilibrium situation. The required conditions are usually satisfied for a star which is not pulsating or rotating rapidly.

Now the chemical composition will change with time at rates which are known; hence, for a star passing relatively slowly through a sequence of configurations, its structure is uniquely determined by its mass, *initial* composition, and age. The Voigt-Russell theorem is very important and useful; for example, it tells us that a star (satisfying the conditions of the theorem) has a unique trace in the Hertzsprung-Russell diagram (see Chapter 6).

✻ 5 ✻ basic data, the hertzsprung-russell diagram and stellar atmospheres

Of what value are the observations in the study of stellar structure and stellar evolution? The answer to this question is obvious to workers in astronomy, but it is not always so obvious to students. The correct answer has been succinctly expressed by M. Schwarzschild in the opening paragraph of his monograph "Structure and Evolution of the Stars," Princeton University Press, 1958.

The basic point is that observations are absolutely necessary for progress in stellar structure and stellar evolution. When we have proceeded without the proper observational foundation, little progress has been made; thus, it is not possible to study stellar evolution in the figurative ivory tower. Thus observations are the "pillars rather than crutches" of the study of stellar evolution.

Now how can we hope to study stellar evolution even with the pillars of observation since, for example, the Sun has an age of some 4.5 billion years? Mankind has a recorded history of at most a few thousand years, and quantitative astrophysics has a history of at most one hundred years. The answer to this question is that (1) indeed, life is going to be difficult, but (2) there is hope provided we take the correct attitude toward the observations. Let us illustrate this point with a fable by J. F. Heard (the original idea has been attributed by Russell, Dugan, and Stewart to J. Herschel). (By permission from J. F. Heard, *J. Roy. Astron. Soc. Can.*, 1957.)

A certain ruler had two teams of philosophers locked up in ivory towers so that they had never seen growing plants or trees. One day he took them to a forest and proposed this contest. These are trees, he said, I will give each team a day to observe them and then I will ask you if they are changing at all, and if so, how. The first group watched carefully, saw no changes and concluded that either the trees were not changing or that they were changing so slowly that no conclusion could be reached from a day's observation. The second group spent their day in frenzied activity, not only watching for growth, but measuring and counting everything they could about the trees. Then for weeks they studied their statistics and summarized their conclusions as follows:

"The trees resemble one another in many ways and differ

mostly in size. We think it likely that the small trees are young and the large ones old because we see some dead big trees but no dead small trees and we observe that sap is flowing upwards in the trees; and many of the big trees are the same size, whereas the small trees are graded in size; so we suppose that trees are being born all the time, grow relatively rapidly to a certain maximum size and then remain at that size for a long time before they die." Needless to say, the second group of philosophers won the contest.

A very convenient way of expressing some observational facts is the popular *Hertzsprung-Russell diagram,* H-R diagram, or temperature-luminosity diagram, which is shown schematically in Figure 5.1. Here are plotted most of the important star types for the study of stellar evolution. Also shown are such stars as white dwarfs, red giants, and the main sequence. In the next two chapters we assemble the observational and theoretical facts required for the construction and understanding of this composite diagram.

5.2 BOLOMETRIC MAGNITUDES AND LUMINOSITIES

Definitions

The bolometric absolute magnitude M_{bol}, shown as the right-hand ordinate in Figure 5.1, is directly related to the luminosity via

$$M_{bol,1} - M_{bol,2} = 2.5 \log \frac{L_2}{L_1} \tag{5.1}$$

which gives the relative magnitude, and to the apparent magnitude via

$$M_{bol} - m_{bol} = 5 - 5 \log D \tag{5.2}$$

where m_{bol} is the apparent bolometric magnitude and D is the distance in parsecs (defined below under *distances*). The apparent bolometric magnitude m_{bol} is the magnitude observed by a de-

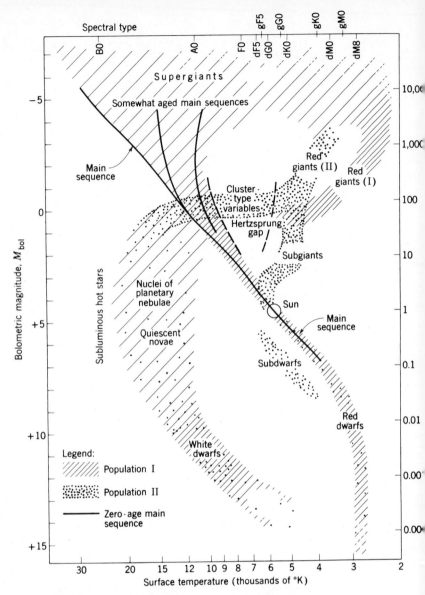

FIGURE 5.1   Hertzsprung-Russell, or temperature-luminosity, diagram (called H-R diagram), showing the regions occupied by stars of various kinds or populations, the main sequence, and the position of the Sun (due to L. Goldberg and E. R. Dyer, Jr.). *From Science in Space by L. V. Berkner and H. Odishaw (eds.). Copyright, 1961. McGraw-Hill Book Company. Used by permission.*

tector outside the atmosphere which records radiation of *all* wavelengths. The absolute magnitude (be it visual, bolometric, etc.) is the apparent magnitude for a distance of 10 parsecs [see Equation (5.2)]. Since the bolometric magnitude refers to the light integrated over all wavelengths, it clearly refers to the total luminosity. The correspondence between M_{bol} and L is set up by observing or determining both quantities for a "standard star" like the Sun; thus the observations are essentially referred to a predetermined standard. For the Sun, we have $M_{bol} = +4.6$ and $L = 3.8 \times 10^{33}$ ergs/sec. We note in passing that Equations (5.1) and (5.2) can be redefined for any restricted wavelength region, such as the visual range; these equations would then relate M_v, m_v, and L_v.

The visual magnitude can be defined in a variety of ways, but the standard for some years has been in the U(ultraviolet), B(blue), and V(visual) system of Johnson and Morgan (see Figure 5.2). The UBV system is fairly well defined, and the

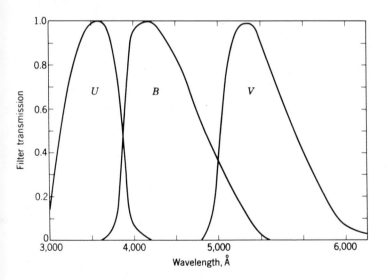

FIGURE 5.2   The filter transmissions on the Johnson-Morgan *UBV* photometric system.

symbols themselves are commonly used to denote the observed magnitudes on this system. The differences of these magnitudes $B - V$, $U - B$, are the "colors"; note that the "colors" are independent of distance (assuming no differential absorption effect).

Bolometric Correction

Normal photometric observations usually yield m_v after atmospheric effects are removed. The distance then gives M_v; note that we briefly consider interstellar absorption in the next subsection. Thus, we need additional information to go from M_v to M_{bol}. The needed quantity is the bolometric correction BC, defined by

$$M_{bol} = M_v + BC \qquad (5.3)$$

The difficulty in determining the BC originates in our lack of knowledge of the variation of the energy output of the star with wavelength caused by the absorption of the Earth's atmosphere; eventually satellite observations should clear this up, but for the present we must muddle through with corrections deduced from ground-based observations. We adopt the compilation given by D. L. Harris III, and it is summarized in Figure 5.3. These figures refer to main-sequence stars and giants and are derived as follows: For the stars of spectral class F5 and later (cooler), the BC is based on the thermocouple observations made by Pettit and Nicholson in 1928. Such observations give the so-called *radiometric magnitude* m_r, which can be accurately extrapolated to outside the atmosphere. The correction to m_{bol} varies between -0.4 and -0.6 mag for the entire spectral range from F5 to M6; hence, the correction is almost independent of the assumed stellar temperature, and the BC should be fairly well determined.

However, the situation for the earlier (hotter) stars is rather different, since here the BC depends entirely on the theoretical predictions of the emergent fluxes from these atmospheres. Since a magnitude difference of 2.5 corresponds to a factor of 10 in the luminosity, the uncertainty for the early-type stars near spectral type B0 ($T_{eff} \approx 30,000°K$) is obvious.

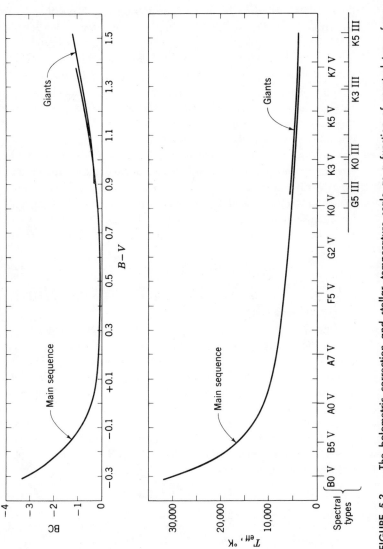

FIGURE 5.3 The bolometric correction and stellar temperature scale as a function of spectral type, from data compiled by D. L. Harris.

Interstellar reddening dims the light of distant stars and changes their colors; it arises because of scattering (and possibly some absorption) by interstellar dust grains. The composition of the dust grains is a subject of discussion; graphite and ice crystals are among the possibilities. Fortunately, the spectral shape of the absorption is known; the absorption (used here in the sense of photons removed from the beam) varies approximately as λ^{-1}, (and hence leading to the term "reddening"). This circumstance generally allows the reddening to be determined from three-color photometry, such as the UBV system.

We show here a particularly neat method of determining the interstellar reddening, valid for main-sequence stars with spectral types earlier than A0. A plot of $U - B$ versus $B - V$ is called a two-color diagram; such a plot (schematic) is shown in Figure 5.4 for main-sequence stars. The intrinsic colors of the early-type stars follow a linear relation called the intrinsic line, which has the equation

$$(U - B)_0 = 3.706 (B - V)_0 \tag{5.4}$$

The subscript 0 is used to designate intrinsic colors (interstellar absorption removed).

Now if we could vary the amount of absorbing material between the observer and the star, the position of the star on the two-color diagram would change with increasing absorption. Because of the relatively simple absorbing properties of the dust, a linear "reddening line" is traced out, which has the equation

$$U - B = 0.886 (B - V) + Q \tag{5.5}$$

where Q is a parameter directly related to $(B - V)_0$ or the spectral type through

$$(B - V)_0 = 0.332Q \tag{5.6}$$

Thus, an observation of $U - B$ and $B - V$ immediately yields Q and thus $(B - V)_0$; then the intrinsic line gives $(U - B)_0$, and the intrinsic colors are determined.

Since we now have both the intrinsic and observed colors, we can form the "color excess" due to absorption, e.g.,

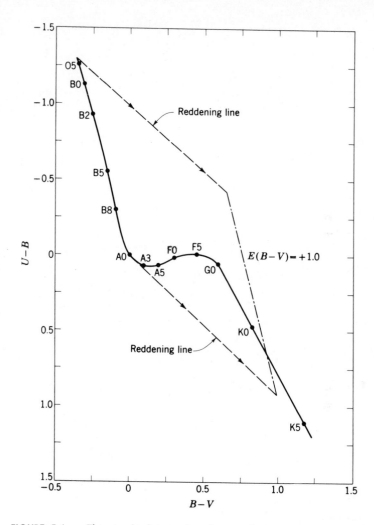

FIGURE 5.4   The standard two-color diagram for main-sequence stars as described in the text. Some sample reddening lines are also shown.

$$E_{B-V} = (B - V) - (B - V)_0 \qquad \textbf{(5.7)}$$

etc. Since the wavelength dependence of the interstellar absorption is known, the ratio R of total to selective absorption can be determined, and one finds

$$R = \frac{A_V}{E_{B-V}} = 3.0 \qquad \text{(5.8)}$$

The quantity A_V is the absorption in magnitudes, which should be subtracted from the observed V to correct for interstellar absorption.

The method outlined here is valid for main-sequence B stars. However, if a group of stars is in a physical cluster at the same distance and if the absorption is uniform across the cluster, the absorption found from the B stars can be applied to all the cluster members.

Distances

The only really accurate distances are those determined for the nearby stars by trigonometric parallaxes. The parallax p of a star is the half-angle of the change in the star's position with respect to the background stars as viewed from opposite sides of the Earth's orbit. The unit of distance in stellar astronomy is the parsec, the distance of a star with parallax of 1 sec of arc ($1''$). For comparison, there are 206,265 AU in a parsec (more fundamentally, there are also the same number of seconds of arc in a radian). One parsec is about 3.26 light-years, or 3.08×10^{18} cm.

No parallax is known which is as large as $1''$; the closest known star, Proxima Centauri, has a parallax of $0.''76$. Beyond 50 parsecs, the uncertainties in the parallax are comparable with the results, and hence the distances are not too accurate. However, within 20 parsecs, over 700 parallaxes are known with an accuracy of about 10 percent. This body of information is the basis for calibrating the indirect methods.

Other purely geometrical methods are available. Some are based on observed proper motions μ, which are given in seconds of arc per year. Over long periods of time the position of a star changes slowly with respect to a fixed coordinate system which is determined by background stars or galaxies. Part of this motion is due to the movement of the Earth as it is carried through space in orbit around the Sun, and part of the motion is due to movement of the star relative to the Sun as a reference point. The effect is analogous to the apparent rate of motion of scenery viewed from a moving car; nearby objects pass quickly while distant objects pass slowly. Distances determined in this manner are termed *statistical parallaxes*. Note that we must have a sufficiently large group of stars to permit removal of the random motions. We return to this discussion in connection with the calibration of the RR Lyrae stars. The tangential (to the line of sight) velocity in kilometers per second is given by

$$T = \frac{4.74\mu}{p} \tag{5.9}$$

where p is the parallax in seconds of arc.

The basic diagram for the determination of parallaxes by the moving-cluster method is shown in Figure 5.5. A moving cluster is a group of stars with parallel or nearly parallel space velocities; when projected on the celestial sphere, the cluster members show proper motions which all point to the convergent point. If the radial velocities of some of the cluster members are known, it is clear that the distance can be found by relating the proper motion to the radial velocity through the angle θ (shown in Figure 5.5). However, the angle θ is simply the angle between the star in question and the convergent point; hence, the parallax is calculable under these conditions. The best-known moving cluster is probably the Hyades, with a well-determined parallax of 0″.025.

The distances to a few isolated stars can be found directly by some other methods (such as observing the radial velocity and angular motion of expanding nova shells); these methods are not applicable to large numbers of stars.

The indirect methods are based on prior knowledge of some properties of the star or the cluster in which it exists. For example, the nearby stars for which trigonometric parallaxes are available can be used to calibrate a color system or a system of spectral classification in terms of luminosity. Thus an accurate spectral class on a well-defined system leads to a so-called *spectroscopic parallax*.

Stellar clusters are of great importance in the study of stellar evolution, and the fact that these stars are all at effectively the same distance enables this very distance to be determined. The

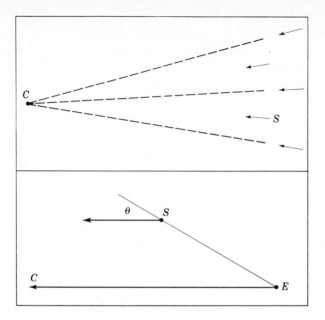

FIGURE 5.5   The moving-cluster diagrams; see the text for discussion. Above: the projection of the star in question (S) and convergent point (C) on the plane of the sky. Below: the projection in the plane containing C, S, and the Earth.

Hertzsprung-Russell diagrams for clusters show definite, reproducible characteristics which can be utilized, since the plot of T_e versus m_v (for example) need only be slid vertically until the characteristic features coincide to determine M_v and thus the luminosity or distance.

These characteristic features are schematically shown in Figure 5.1. For galactic clusters (Population I, younger stars; see Section 6.6), the lower main sequence (in the vicinity of the Sun) appears to form a unique relation in the H-R diagram; this relation is called the initial or zero-age main sequence. Thus, superposition of the lower main sequence for a given cluster and the lower main sequence for the Hyades (for which an accurate parallax is known by the moving-cluster method) gives the absolute magnitude.

For globular clusters (Population II, older stars; see Section 6.6), the situation is more complex. We can superimpose the observations on the initial main sequence for Population I stars, but this could be a poor approximation, because the absolute magnitude of the two populations is probably different. A better method is to fix the absolute magnitude scale by means of the variable stars found in the "horizontal branch" of the globular cluster H-R diagram (see Figure 5.1). These stars are known as cluster variables and also as RR Lyrae stars after the nearby class star in the constellation of Lyra. The average distance, i.e., a statistical parallax, of these nearby cluster-type variables can be inferred from their proper motions (as discussed above). On the average the random velocities of this group of stars will cancel out, and the remaining average component of proper motion is due mainly to the Sun's motion through the galaxy. Since the Sun moves some 4.2 AU per year relative to the close neighboring stars, a wait of a few tens of years provides an extremely long base line for the measurement of a "parallax." However, we reemphasize that the star's own random motion is superimposed on the effect which we seek, and hence the method is a statistical one. The absolute magnitude of the cluster-type variables, or RR Lyrae stars, lies near +0.7, and thus distances to globular clusters such as M3 can be inferred. Surprisingly and fortunately, the different methods described here give much the same result when applied to M3; hence, luminosities of globular cluster stars can be determined with some certainty.

5.3 EFFECTIVE TEMPERATURES

The effective temperature of a star is defined as the temperature of a blackbody of the same radius which produces the same total luminosity; notice that a star need not radiate like a blackbody to have a well-determined effective temperature. The effective temperature is easily determined only for the Sun.

From Luminosities and Radii

Equation (1.1) gives a star's luminosity in terms of the radius and effective temperature; thus, the effective temperature T_{eff} can be easily determined for stars of known luminosity (see above) if the radius has been determined from studies of binary stars or from interferometric observations (see Section 5.4). The intensity of a star's surface [units $=$ ergs/(cm^2)(sec)(steradian)] can be found and compared with that of the Sun if only an angular diameter is known.

These are the direct methods for determination of T_{eff}, but unfortunately they apply only to a limited number of stars. D. L. Harris III in a recent tabulation lists only *eleven* fundamental effective temperature determinations, and this figure includes the Sun; only *five* are main-sequence stars! The radii of stars determined in this fashion serve, nevertheless, as a valuable check on the indirect methods.

From Colors

A "color" consists of the difference in magnitudes of observations of a star taken at two different effective wavelengths. It is clear that a Planck curve can be assumed for the variation of flux with wavelength and the temperature in the Planck formula varied until agreement with the observations is obtained. Such a procedure determines a "color temperature."

A more precise color temperature can be defined through the absolute gradient defined by

$$\phi = 5\lambda - \frac{d(\log_e F_\lambda)}{d(1/\lambda)} \tag{5.10}$$

where λ is the wavelength in centimeters and F_λ is the flux of the source (per unit wavelength interval). This can be rewritten in terms of the Planck formula [see Equation (2.8); note that for the conversion from frequency to wavelength, Equation (2.8) must be written in terms of $B_\nu(T)\,d\nu$ and that *both* B_ν and $d\nu$ must be converted to wavelength units to write $B_\lambda\,d\lambda$ for F_λ (proportional to B_λ) as

$$\phi = \frac{c_2}{T_c}(1 - e^{-c_2/\lambda T_c})^{-1} \tag{5.11}$$

where T_c is the color temperature and $c_2 = h/ck$ (recall that h is Planck's constant, c is the velocity of light, and k is Boltzmann's constant). Color temperatures determined for several wavelengths can be compared with the adopted effective temperature scale; the color temperatures are encouraging, but not of good accuracy.

This situation suggests a combination of the color temperatures and the fundamental data whereby observed colors are used as an interpolation relation to bridge the gaps between the fundamental values. This is the technique used in determining the color $(B - V)$ versus T_{eff} relation given in Figure 5.3; specifically, stars hotter than the Sun in Figure 5.3 have the reciprocal effective temperature varying smoothly with $B - V$, while stars cooler than the Sun have T_{eff} varying smoothly with $B - R$ [this color is essentially (blue) − (red) with the effective red wavelength being about 7,200 Å]. The choice of the red color is natural, since the cooler stars have most of their radiation in the longer wavelength regions.

From Spectra

In principle, it would be possible to study stellar spectra carefully and to determine the temperature necessary for the excitation and ionization of the lines and stages of ionization observed. Such a procedure would require a substantial investigation for each star, and the answer need not be accurately related to the effective temperature.

It is simpler to use a system of classification of spectra as an interpolation device between fundamental effective temperatures. The classifications can also be intercompared with the colors and their associated T_{eff}'s; this last comparison is valuable, since the colors of stars of a given spectral type can be accurately determined. The spectral type versus T_{eff} relation is shown in Figure 5.3.

To give some insight into the problem of stellar spectra and their classification, we briefly review the Yerkes MK system. An important part of the philosophy of this system is that standard stars define the classes; hence, a star correctly classified on this system remains so even if the physical parameters, such as the luminosity and effective temperature, change because of a recalibration.

Figure 5.6 shows a particular region of the spectrum of stars ranging from type B to type M, which are the hottest and coolest type stars, respectively, considered on the usual classification scheme. The full normal range is (in order of decreasing T_{eff}) O,B,A,F,G,K, and M; the temperatures corresponding to various spectral classes are shown in Figure 5.3. In practice, it is possible to classify spectra to better than a class, and subclasses are used; thus, the Sun is classified as G2 V. The roman numeral denotes the luminosity class (V indicates a main-sequence star); further discussion of luminosity classes is given below. Note that not all subclasses exist; e.g., there are no F9 stars.

The classification is based on visual inspection and estimation of the ratios of line strengths. In practice, this is done at a microscope, where the spectrum to be classified can be viewed with a standard spectrum immediately beside it for comparison. Thus one seeks the standard spectrum which matches the unknown, the "match" being determined by the criteria of specific line-strength ratios given for the MK system in the Yerkes "Atlas of Stellar Spectra." Hence, we limit ourselves here to a qualitative description of the spectra; the interpretation is deferred to the last section in this chapter.

The hottest normal stars, those of type O, show an uncrowded continuum interspersed with lines of highly ionized atoms, such as He II, Si IV, and N III; occasionally some emission is observed. Hydrogen lines are observed, but they are weak. The H and K lines of Ca II are occasionally observed, but they are sharp and of interstellar origin.

In the spectra of B stars, He II lines disappear while He I remains strong and the hydrogen lines get stronger. There are also some lines of Si III, Si II, and Mg II, but the spectrum is still quite uncluttered.

The spectra of A stars show primarily hydrogen lines, which reach their maximum at A0 and stay strong through the A stars; the helium lines are gone. Lines of Mg II and Si II decrease, while lines of Ca II and Fe II appear and increase.

In the F stars, the spectrum begins to faintly show myriads of absorption lines of the metals; the H and K lines of Ca II increase rapidly. Hydrogen lines grow weaker but are still prominent.

The solar-type spectrum is found in the G stars. The lines of Ca II increase to a maximum; hydrogen lines are present but

weak. The spectrum is very rich, being filled with many neutral
iron lines. Molecular bands of CH and CN appear and increase in strength. The K stars follow the general trends established in the G stars with the hydrogen lines now quite weak. The λ4,226 line of Ca I becomes strong in the K stars, while Ca II lines wane.

The spectra of the M stars are dominated by neutral metal lines (such as λ4,226 of Ca I) and by molecular bands [such as the strong titanium oxide (TiO) bands].

We anticipate the results of Section 5.6 by noting that (1) the spectral sequence is a temperature sequence, and (2) the appearance and disappearance of lines of a given element generally does not mean a genuine difference in chemical composition.

Certain absorption lines are stronger in the spectra of the more luminous stars than in the spectra of the corresponding main-sequence stars; these lines then serve as luminosity criteria, as illustrated in Figure 5.7. If these luminosity classes can be calibrated (for example, on a few nearby stars with trigonometric parallaxes), then a star need only be bright enough to enable its spectrum to be taken, and a fairly accurate estimate of its luminosity is available; distances thus determined are called *spectroscopic parallaxes*. They are of great value in probing the galaxy for distances greater than 100 parsecs.

The luminosity classes on the MK system are Ia, most luminous supergiants; Ib, less luminous supergiants; II, bright giants; III, normal giants; IV, subgiants; V, main-sequence stars (often called dwarfs). The calibration of the most luminous supergiants (which depends partly on the space motions produced by galactic rotation) is uncertain. The physical basis of the luminosity criteria is discussed at the end of this chapter.

The MK system is thus a two-dimensional system which gives, when calibrated, the absolute magnitude and effective temperature. This system is applicable mainly to Population I stars, and clearly another parameter or dimension is needed. The extra parameter should be representative of population or chemical composition. Such systems, based on photometric measurements, have been devised, for example, by Chalonge and Strömgren. These advanced systems show that stars with enhanced radiation in the ultraviolet wavelength region (termed an "ultraviolet excess") are deficient in their abundances of metals, and hence are probably stars of Population II. This subject is explored further in Chapter 6.

Finally, we mention that there are many stars which are not strictly classifiable in these systems. Some of these are very hot, such as the Wolf-Rayet stars, which show broad emission lines of carbon or nitrogen. Some are of intermediate temperature, such as the magnetic variables where lines are strongly influenced by the Zeeman effect. Some are stars of low temperature, such as the stars labeled R, N, and S; these letters are sometimes appended to the normal MK sequence. Stars of class S, for example, show molecular bands of ZrO, YO, and LaO and, in addition, atomic lines of technetium (half-life of some 3×10^5 years, not found naturally on the Earth). Finally, there are the white dwarfs, which have a spectrum composed mainly of extremely wide absorption lines of hydrogen; the great width arises from pressure broadening, caused by the exceedingly high densities in the atmosphere of the white dwarf.

Before leaving the domain of the H-R diagram, we wish to emphasize one extremely important point. There is considerable difference in the observed H-R diagram, for example, m_v versus spectral type, and the nice, neat, theoretical H-R diagram, that is, M_{bol} versus T_{eff}. Many assumptions, corrections, and manipulations lie between the two diagrams, and these problems should be kept firmly in mind.

5.4   RADII

In this section and the next, we discuss the determination of stellar radii and masses; these data were known with ease for the Sun, but we shall find the situation far more difficult for the other stars. Inferred radii of stars range from about the size of the Moon to nearly the radius of the orbit of Saturn.

From Luminosities and Effective Temperatures

Equation (1.1) gives a star's luminosity in terms of its radius and effective temperature. In the preceding sections, we have outlined the ways of determining L and T_{eff}; for these stars, the radii can be readily calculated. Roughly speaking, the loci of constant radii run parallel to the main sequence.

However, these determinations are not basic, and the errors in L and T_{eff} are carried into the determination of r.

From interferometry

Some years ago it was found that some relatively nearby supergiants and giants had radii sufficiently large to be determined with an interferometer. The two halves of the star were considered separate stars and the usual interferometric techniques applied to determine the apparent separation. Correction formulas (including the effects of limb darkening) then give the angular radii. Since most of these stars are close enough to have rather good parallax determinations, the linear radii follow immediately; the early work with reliable results amounted to some half-dozen stars (Michelson and Pease). The method has been extended to Sirius (Brown and Twiss).

These data are meager, but they serve as valuable checks on the other methods.

From binaries

The systems which are of interest here are double-lined spectroscopic binaries which are also eclipsing binaries. The solution of the spectroscopic system gives $M_1 \sin^3 \iota$, $M_2 \sin^3 \iota$, and $a \sin \iota$, where M_1 and M_2 are the masses, a the semimajor axis, and ι is the inclination of the orbital plane to the plane of the sky. The analysis converts the oscillations of the lines of the two components to velocities (via the doppler effect), and these velocities are analyzed on the basis of revolution about each other under gravitational attraction.

The shape of the light curve of an eclipsing binary system permits the determination of r_1/a, r_2/a, and ι, where r_1 and r_2 are the radii. The combination of the two solutions yields both masses and both radii.

The problem here is that few, if any, double stars are considered "entirely normal" (see Section 7.4). Only about a dozen systems survive stringent criteria of "reliability." Again, these are of value as calibrations.

Thus, the vast majority of stellar radii are found from luminosities and effective temperatures, with a relatively small number of direct determinations serving as checks.

5.5 MASSES

For only one star, the Sun, is the mass known with high accuracy. It is an uphill struggle for other stars.

From spectroscopic-eclipsing binaries

These systems, described above under the heading of radii (Section 5.4), give the masses of both components for so-called *reliable* cases. This provides some 24 mass determinations; the results are shown in Figure 5.8.

From visual binaries

Kepler's third law can be written as

$$\frac{a^3}{P^2} = \frac{G}{4\pi^2}(M_1 + M_2) \tag{5.12}$$

where M_1 and $M_2 =$ masses, g
$\quad\quad P =$ period, sec
$\quad\quad G =$ constant of gravitation
$\quad\quad a =$ semimajor axis, cm

If the period is determined, by means of continuous observations through one or more revolutions, and the system is close enough for a trigonometric parallax, the sum of the masses can be determined.

If the mass ratios can be found by determining the motion of each component about the center of gravity of the system, the mass ratio can be combined with the sum to yield individual masses. The problem here is that the measurements must be referred to a system of background stars to determine the mass ratio; the simpler differential measurements adequate for the period will not suffice, although the parallax and mass-ratio determinations usually come together.

There are roughly 20 systems with good elements and parallaxes greater than 0.1. Figure 5.8 is a composite diagram giving the direct mass determinations versus absolute bolometric magnitude M_{bol}; this is the empirical mass-luminosity relation, a rather narrow sequence extending from $M_{bol} = 0$ to $M_{bol} = +11$. This sequence can be represented by

$$M_{bol} = 4.6 - 10.0 \log M \ (M_{bol} < +7.5)$$
$$M_{bol} = 5.2 - 6.9 \log M \ (M_{bol} > +7.5)$$

(5.13)

If we write generally,

$$M_{bol} = \log A - B \log M$$

(5.14)

and

$$L = aM^p$$

(5.15)

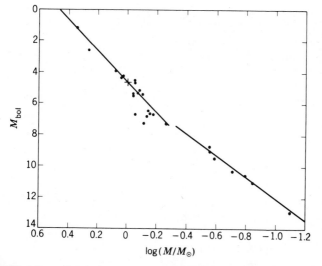

FIGURE 5.8   The main-sequence mass-luminosity relation for stars with high weight; the lines shown correspond to the expressions given in Equation (5.13). The Sun is marked as a cross.

$$P = 0.4B \qquad \text{(5.16)}$$

Hence, Equations (5.13) correspond to $P = 2.8$ and $P = 4.0$, which compares well with our crude theoretical estimate of $P = 3.0$ given at the end of Chapter 4.

5.6 STELLAR ATMOSPHERES; THEIR QUALITATIVE INTERPRETATION

In the previous sections of the chapter, we have discussed the characteristics of stellar atmospheres, such as their spectra and colors. To a certain extent, however, a stellar atmosphere is a skin phenomenon and merely reveals the more basic properties of the interior. These more basic properties of the interior determine the manner in which a star evolves—the subject of Chapter 6. Here we give the physical basis of the qualitative understanding of stellar spectra and colors.

We should also remember that the study of atmospheres is crucial in the determination of the abundances of the elements—the important Population parameter. The basic principles of abundance determinations have been described in Chapter 2.

Colors

Since we know that the spectral sequence is a temperature sequence, the variation of, say, $B - V$ with spectral type does not require explanation beyond that given above (Section 5.3). However, the two-color plot, $(U - B)$ versus $(B - V)$, requires a word of discussion; here we consider the two-color diagram for main-sequence stars.

Because the two colors both increase as the temperature decreases (consider them color temperatures), the general trend of the two-color diagram (Figure 5.4) from the upper left to the lower right is entirely to be expected. Crudely, one can attribute it to the shift in the peak of the Planck curve toward the red as the temperature decreases. The pronounced dip near A0 needs explanation.

This dip arises because the U filter (see Figure 5.2) covers part of the Balmer series and the Balmer continuum ($\lambda < 3{,}646$ Å). Hydrogen absorption increases very rapidly in the B stars as one goes toward later spectral type; it reaches a maximum at about A2 and then declines. Absorption by hydrogen ceases to be important near G0. Thus the dip is caused by hydrogen absorption, an effect not present in perfect Planck-law radiators. These remarks qualitatively explain the main-sequence two-color diagram.

The explanation given can be checked by considering the two-color diagram for another class of stars, such as supergiants (luminosity class I). In supergiants the hydrogen absorption (while reaching a maximum near A0) is much less pronounced, and this manifests itself as a much smaller dip in the two-color plot for supergiants.

Finally, we point out that, in spite of its proven usefulness, the two-color plot can be immediately improved upon. The use of the B color in both coordinates must decrease the diagram's ability to resolve different types of stars; clearly, a two-color diagram with a total of four colors is desirable.

Spectra

The spectral sequence again is clearly a temperature sequence; the lowest temperatures show lines of low excitation potential and molecular bands. The stars of highest temperature show lines of high ionization and excitation potential. This situation is clearly shown in Figure 5.9, which shows a plot of the excitation energy of particular lines versus the spectral type of the maximum intensity for the line(s). Lines of hydrogen are found in many classes of stars simply because hydrogen is so abundant.

While there are genuine abundance differences in stars, these differences generally do *not* explain the appearance and disappearance of lines through the spectral sequence. Rather, if we consider a resonance line (a line whose lowest state is the ground state), the characteristics of the spectral sequence can be explained by the appearance and disappearance of the various ions of a given atomic

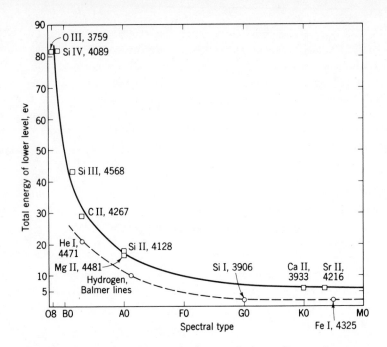

FIGURE 5.9 A plot of the spectral type of various line maxima versus the total energy (ionization + excitation) of the lower level (of the line in question) reckoned from the ground level of the neutral atom. *After J. Dufay.*

species. This behavior is calculable from the Saha equation, viz.,

$$\frac{x}{(1-x)} P_e = \frac{2u_{r+1}}{u_r} \frac{(2\pi m_e)^{3/2}}{h^3} (kT)^{5/2} e^{-I_r/kT} \qquad (5.17)$$

where P_e = electron pressure
u_r = partition function with $(2u_{r+1})/u_r \approx 1$ (generally)
h = Planck's constant
k = Boltzmann's constant
m_e = electron mass
T = temperature
I_r = ionization potential
x = fraction of the element $(r+1)$ times ionized
$1-x$ = fraction of the element (r) times ionized
and the subscript r refers to the r times ionized constituent.

Consider now the lines formed from the ground state of Ca I
($\lambda 4,226$) and Ca II (H and K lines); we simply compute the relative number of atoms in each state of ionization, since the appropriate oscillator strengths are roughly the same and since an entirely negligible number of atoms are in excited states. The results of a calculation of x and $1 - x$ for calcium with P_e as parameter are shown in Figure 5.10. Compare, for example, the results for an electron pressure of 10 bars with Figure 5.9; the agreement is quite encouraging, and we may regard the main features of the spectral sequence as explained by the Saha equation.

If the line in question originates from an excited state (such as many lines of neutral iron) and if it can be regarded as formed in LTE, then the Boltzmann formula can be used to compute the number of atoms in the required excited state, viz.,

$$\frac{N_m}{N_n} = \frac{g_m}{g_n} \exp\left(-\frac{h\nu_{mn}}{kT}\right) \qquad \textbf{(5.18)}$$

Here $h\nu_{mn}$ is the energy difference between the levels m and n, and the g's are the statistical weights. Virtually all atoms of a given stage of ionization are found in the ground state; then Equation

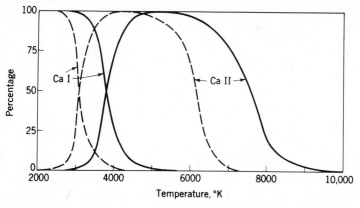

FIGURE 5.10   The percentage of calcium in the ionization stages Ca I and Ca II as a function of temperature. The solid line is for an electron pressure of 10 bars and the dashed line for an electron pressure of 0.1 bars. See the text for discussion.

(5.18) can be used to calculate the small fraction of atoms in a given excited state. The variation with temperature of a line originating from an excited state is readily calculated (as above for a line originating from the ground state) from Equations (5.17) and (5.18).

We now return to the curves shown in Figure 5.10 for the lines originating from the ground state. The curve calculated for $P_e = 0.1$ bar shows (schematically) the variation with luminosity class, namely, that a given degree of ionization is reached at a lower temperature for a lower density. Physically, this arises because recombinations go as $N_e{}^2$ (where N_e is the electron density per cubic centimeter), while ionizations are produced by photons, which depend only on the temperature. Thus, a reduction of the density greatly reduces the recombination rate, while (for roughly the same temperature) the ionization rate is unchanged. Thus, equilibrium is established at a lower temperature.

Now the classification of spectra is based on the ratios of line strengths, and hence, roughly speaking, stars of the same spectral type have atoms at the same degree of ionization. Now if the density is lower, the electron pressure is lower, and thus the temperature is lower. This effect is well established (see Figure 5.3), and hence giants have a slightly lower effective temperature than main-sequence stars of the same spectral class.

The fact that the density in the atmospheres of giants and supergiants is lower than in the atmospheres of the corresponding main-sequence stars provides a qualitative explanation of the line-strength criteria used to establish luminosities. Ionic species are more likely to be found in giants (because, as mentioned above, the ionization remains the same for the same temperature, while the decreased density reduces the recombination); thus, ionic lines should be stronger in giants than in main-sequence stars of the same spectral type. However, giants and main-sequence stars of the same spectral type have similar appearing spectra and, hence, approximately the same average degree of ionization. Thus, the desired effect shows up in the lines of easily ionized atoms. One example is strontium; the lines of Sr II are stronger in giants than in main-sequence stars.

The situation for the hydrogen lines is reversed; hydrogen lines are weaker in giants and supergiants than in main-sequence stars, as we mentioned in the beginning of this section in the discussion of the "hydrogen dip" in the two-color diagram. The effect mentioned occurs because electric fields due to ions and electrons broaden the hydrogen lines (Stark effect); this broadening effectively shifts atoms away from the line center and allows additional absorption. However, the Stark effect is very much reduced in giants and supergiants because of the low densities, and hence the broadening is greatly reduced. This situation confines the absorption to the line center where saturation (see the discussion of the curve of growth in Chapter 2) can occur, and the total absorption is greatly reduced.

In summary, the general differences in spectra between giants and main-sequence stars (see Figure 5.7) are attributable to lower densities in the atmosphere of the former. Now the lower densities in giants are the direct result of the vastly larger diameters of these stars compared with main-sequence stars; the larger diameters with approximately the same effective temperatures produce a greatly increased luminosity in giants over main-sequence stars. Thus, a detailed comparison of line strengths yields a knowledge of pressure, hence diameter, and hence luminosity. This is the basis of the luminosity classification where I are the supergiants, III are the giants, and V are the main-sequence stars.

We described in Chapter 1 some of the events and discoveries which led to the concept of stellar evolution. Here we utilize the developments discussed in the preceding chapters to sketch contemporary ideas of stellar evolution and to compare these ideas with relevant observational data.

6.1 INTRODUCTION

In Chapter 4, we discussed the set of equations describing a star in an equilibrium state. In the consideration of an evolving star the time variable t is introduced; hence, in principle, the equations given in Chapter 4 must be modified for a time-dependent situation, and an additional equation(s) for the time must be given. Normally, one considers that evolution takes place through a sequence of equilibrium states, and thus the basic structural equations given in Chapter 4 need not be altered. Even if modifications are required in these equations, such changes are headaches in practice, but not in principle.

The changes in the star due to evolution can be represented in the functions dX/dt and dY/dt, where these are the time rates of change of the mass fraction for hydrogen and helium, respectively; these rates are known from the energy-generation formulas. Hydrogen is destroyed through the proton-proton chain and the carbon cycle; helium is created via these same reactions and is destroyed in the triple-alpha reaction.

An initial model is computed for the given mass and chemical composition; it is then evolved a small amount by taking account of the changes in X and Y and a new model computed, and so on.

With these techniques, we should be able to compute the tracks of stars in the H-R diagram. We should bear in mind that in large part the aim of the theory of stellar evolution is to explain the myriad of facts contained in the observational H-R diagrams. We begin with a description of the evolution of the Sun.

At the onset, we should emphasize the great complexity of the calculations which describe the evolution of stars; stellar evolution is a discipline made possible by the era of large, fast electronic computers. In the study of stellar structure discussed in Chapter 4, we found that we had a problem of seven equations in seven unknowns, to say nothing of the large amounts of fairly exotic physics required. In stellar evolution, we have the same equations plus the time variations and the equations to describe them. Thus, it may not always be possible to give simple physical explanations for all the phenomena under discussion, although we shall make every effort where possible.

6.2 THE EVOLUTION OF THE SUN

Besides our natural enhanced interest in the Sun because of our proximity and our relatively high state of knowledge, we consider the Sun because we believe that we have an accurate estimate of its *age*.

This age estimate comes from geological evidence (and studies of meteorites) and is 4.5×10^9 years—a figure which gives the age of the solidification of the crust of the Earth. This value is based on the study of the ratio of certain radioactive elements (uranium and thorium) to their final decay products (notably lead). It is considered unlikely that this age differs significantly from the age of the Sun.

Formation of the Sun

Contemporary opinion on star formation holds that objects called protostars are formed as condensations from the interstellar gas. This condensation process is very difficult theoretically, and no essential theoretical understanding can be claimed; in fact, some theoretical evidence argues strongly against the possibility of star formation. However, we know that the stars exist, and we must do our best to account for them.

Evidence for contemporary or comparatively recent star formation comes from the mere existence of O and B stars. Now the life of the Sun on the main sequence (i.e., essentially in its present condition) is about 10^{10} years, as we show below. This time is determined by the amount of fuel (hydrogen) available and the rate at which it is being burned. A typical O or B star may have a mass of $30M_\odot$ and a luminosity of 10^5 times that of the Sun.

Thus, compared with the Sun, these very luminous stars have only 30 times more fuel, while they burn it 10^5 times more rapidly. It is clear then that they have main-sequence lifetimes of only some 10^6 to 10^7 years. It is also clear that stars less massive than the Sun must have enormous ages (consider the form of the mass-luminosity relation).

Now from the observational viewpoint we can study the problem as follows: (1) Where or what are the likely places of star formation? (2) Where are the obviously young stars (such as O stars, discussed just above, which have very short ages as determined by their enormous luminosities) found? The answer to these questions seems to be in the young clusters or associations which, besides containing young (O and B type) stars, also contain gas, dust, and less luminous nebulous objects, such as the Herbig-Haro objects and T Tauri stars. It is thought that virtually all star formation in the present epoch of the galaxy occurs in such clusters or associations. The field stars then arise through gravitational disruption of the cluster (probably by the tidal action of passing gas clouds). This hypothesis helps explain the relative rarity of old clusters. Star formation may not have been confined to clusters in earlier evolutionary epochs of the galaxy (see Section 6.6).

The Herbig-Haro objects show on photographs as diffuse patches, and these may be protostars at a very early stage. The T Tauri stars are stellar in character; they show emission lines, interpreted as being caused by an enveloping nebula, and their lines show broadening, which can be interpreted as being caused by rapid rotation (thought to be a property of young stars, see just below). Therefore, the first evolutionary sequence may be [Herbig-Haro object] $\rightarrow$ [T Tauri star] $\rightarrow$ [Sun].

Consider now some of the problems involved in the contraction toward the main sequence; this is the so-called Kelvin-Helmholtz stage, where the energy comes from the gravitational potential via contraction. The problem of the angular momentum is a serious one. Typically, one considers that a protostar originates from a cloud some 10^{19} cm in diameter, which would then have a surface rotational velocity of about 10^{-1} km/sec, caused by differential galactic rotation. An unhindered contraction of such a cloud to a body of stellar dimensions with conservation of angular momentum would lead to surface velocities exceeding the velocity of light.

Since this result is clearly absurd, ways of disposing of the angular momentum must be considered. One way is for the star to bifurcate into a double-star system (or multiple system) or to form a planetary system. This latter possibility could apply, at least partially, to the solar system, since the Sun contains only ~ 1 percent of the angular momentum of the solar system (Jupiter and Saturn contain almost all the rest). The second way is to couple the Sun to the surrounding interstellar medium by means of the magnetic field. Here, the excess angular momentum is gradually deposited in the interstellar medium. Thus, young stars may indeed be more rapidly rotating than their older descendants, as may be the case for the T Tauri stars mentioned above.

Let us now consider the broad outlines of the contraction to the main sequence. The thermal or internal energy of a star is

$$U = \int_0^{R*} \left[\frac{3}{2} \frac{kT(r)}{m} \right] 4\pi \, \rho(r) \, r^2 \, dr \qquad (6.1)$$

where k = Boltzmann's constant
R_* = radius of the star
T = temperature
ρ = density
m = average particle mass (approximately one-half the mass of the hydrogen atom)
r = distance from the center of the star
The gravitational potential energy is

$$\Omega = - \int_0^{R*} \left[\frac{M(r) \, G}{r} \right] 4\pi \, \rho(r) \, r^2 \, dr \qquad (6.2)$$

where G is the gravitational constant and $M(r)$ is the mass contained in the sphere of radius r. Now the virial theorem for a star in equilibrium states that the internal and potential energies are related by

$$2U + \Omega = 0 \qquad (6.3)$$

This theorem is basically statistical in nature and is important in classical mechanics; it holds (as stated) for an isolated system of mass points in an inverse-square central-force field under a large variety of conditions. For example, it holds for the motion of the planets about the Sun (see the Review Questions and Problems for this chapter).

We proceed under the assumption of homology; that is, the star's radius decreases, but the mass distribution remains the same. Thus, as a star contracts (that is, r decreases), half of the increase in the gravitational potential energy [Equation (6.2)] goes into the star's luminosity and half into the internal energy because of the virial theorem [Equation (6.3)]. Since the relative mass distribution does not change, and since the internal energy [Equation (6.1)] must increase to satisfy Equation (6.3), we see that the temperature must increase. This basic pattern continues until the star's central temperature becomes $\sim 10^7$ °K; then nuclear energy sources can supply the energy required for the star's luminosity. This stage of near-stability is called the main sequence (see Figure 5.1), where the Sun and other stars spend the major portion of their lifetimes.

The details of the pre-main-sequence contraction are rather interesting. After the "traditional" Kelvin-Helmholtz stage, in which the star moves essentially from right to left in the H-R diagram, the star enters the so-called Hyashi stage, which is characterized by a star in convective equilibrium and by movement in the H-R diagram which is essentially from top to bottom. As the star nears the main sequence, a radiative core develops and grows. This development signals the switchover to a radiative model, which then evolves from right to left and slightly upward toward the main sequence. The final step onto the main sequence involves a turndown of a few tenths of a bolometric magnitude. At this point the "initial" Sun begins life on the main sequence.

The Main-sequence Stage

The initial Sun would be homogeneous throughout, with the values X, Y, and Z being constant at the photospheric value. Inspection of Figure 4.2 shows how the mass fraction of hydrogen X has decreased in the central regions of the Sun because of

nuclear reactions. How else does the present Sun differ from the
initial model?

Basically, main-sequence evolution keeps the Sun near the main sequence but moving toward higher luminosity and the red-giant region. Representative values for the Sun, with the subscript p denoting the present Sun and the subscript i denoting the initial model, are

1. Luminosity, $L_p/L_i = 1.6$
2. Radius, $R_p/R_i \approx 1.04$
3. Effective temperature, $T_{eff,p}/T_{eff,i} \approx 1.1$

Changes in the overall structure of the Sun are thought to be minor. For example, the hydrogen convection zone begins at $r/R_\odot = 0.88$ in the initial Sun and at $r/R_\odot = 0.86$ in the present Sun.

Now what is the future fate of the Sun? Eventually, it will leave the area of the main sequence and move into the region of the red dwarfs. This event is significant because it occurs directly because of the development of a nonhomogeneous Sun. It is possible to construct homogeneous evolving models of the Sun where the decrease in X due to the nuclear reactions is spread uniformly throughout the Sun. Such models evolve toward higher L and T_{eff} along a track essentially parallel to the main sequence. Since the red giants exist, they are strong evidence for non-homogeneous evolution.

The time spent by a star on or very near the main sequence is given by the Schönberg-Chandrasekhar (S-C) limit, which states that the isothermal helium core cannot exceed approximately one-tenth the total mass of the star. Physically, the star or evolved Sun has difficulty maintaining a temperature gradient steep enough to bridge the gap between the high central temperature and the surface temperature. We may recall that a complete isothermal gas sphere has an infinite mass. Hence, the outer layers of the star have increasing difficulty in maintaining the temperature gradient between the core and the surface as the size of the core increases, and if this situation were to continue, the star could find that it would be unable to fit an envelope onto the isothermal core. Now the star has better sense than to permit this dilemma, and it responds by lowering the core temperature—thus allowing the fitting of the envelope. But with the new, lower temperature, and hence lower pressure, the core cannot support the weight of the outer layers. In the heavier stars, the core immediately contracts; in the lighter stars, the situation is more complex, as is explained in due course.

The time required for some 10 percent of the mass of the star to be deposited in the isothermal helium core can be estimated from the energy requirements and the luminosity. The rate of energy production is related to the mass conversion and luminosity by

$$dE = 0.007 \, MXc^2 \, dq = L \, dt \qquad \textbf{(6.4)}$$

where E = energy

M = mass of the star

X = mass fraction for hydrogen

dq = fraction of the mass burned in time dt

This equation can be solved for the time and integrated to give

$$T_{ms} = 0.007 \, Mc^2 \int_{q=0}^{q=q(S-C)} X \, \frac{dq}{L} \qquad \textbf{(6.5)}$$

Thus, with $q(S - C) \approx 1/10$ and the models, one can readily compute T_{ms}.

An approximate solution to this equation has been given by A. R. Sandage as

$$T_{ms} = 1.1 \times 10^{10} \, \frac{(M/M_\odot)}{(L/L_\odot)} \qquad \text{years} \qquad \textbf{(6.6)}$$

This formula readily gives the main-sequence time scale for the Sun of 11 billion years; since the present age is 4.5 billion years, the Sun has some 6.5 billion years left before it rapidly leaves the main-sequence area and moves into the red-giant region. The main-sequence ages of stars of various spectral types are shown in Table 6.1.

Note that the ages given for $M_*/M_\odot < 2$ should be considered illustrative, since (as mentioned above) the strict Schönberg-Chandrasekhar theory does not apply to the lower main sequence;

TABLE 6.1   MAIN-SEQUENCE AGES OF STARS

SPECTRAL TYPE	$M_*/M_\odot$	$L_*/L_\odot$	T_{ms}, years
O7.5	30	8×10^4	4×10^6
B0	16	1×10^4	2×10^7
A0	3	60	6×10^8
F0	1.5	6	3×10^9
G2	1	1	1×10^{10}
K0	0.8	0.4	2×10^{10}
M0	0.5	0.06	9×10^{10}
M5	0.2	0.01	2×10^{11}

we return to this point in the discussion of the evolution of the Sun into the giant stage.

Evolution into the Giant Stage

After the Sun passes the Schönberg-Chandrasekhar limit, its evolution should proceed fairly rapidly as follows: at first the core, which is partially electron degenerate (i.e., the pressure is composed of contributions from the partially degenerate electrons and nondegenerate nuclei—see Section 4.3), can support the outer layers. This is the departure from the strict Schönberg-Chandrasekhar theory for the lower main sequence. Here we have, then, a partially degenerate core, a shallow, shell-like area where hydrogen in the envelope is burned, and the hydrogen envelope itself. As this model evolves, the core grows in size, the envelope expands in radius, and the track on the H-R diagram moves up and to the right, i.e., into the giant and supergiant region. Presumably the expansion of the envelope occurs because the temperature gradient is increased by the shell burning.

When the core contains some half of the mass, the luminosity of the Sun will have increased by 10^2 to 10^3, and because of this large luminosity, the remaining hydrogen is burned at an extremely fast (fractional) rate. The result is that eventually the core can no longer carry the weight of the envelope, and a situation (not unlike the case described for heavier stars) arises which leads to contraction of the core; this contraction raises the temperature of the core, and presently helium burning (via the triple-alpha reaction) begins. The beginning of helium burning is generally held to be the end of evolution into the red-giant region. A red-giant model is shown in Figure 4.7.

Postgiant Evolution and the Death of the Sun

We should emphasize at the onset that this phase of the evolution of the Sun is very uncertain. However, the advent of helium burning is thought to end evolution into the red-giant region and, in fact, reverse the direction of motion in the H-R diagram. If, for example, convection becomes important throughout the star after the onset of helium burning, the tendency would be toward a homogeneous model. We may recall from our previous discussion that a homogeneous star would find itself along or near the initial main sequence. Thus, the Sun could conceivably return to the vicinity of the main sequence in this fashion, but again the situation is quite uncertain.

White dwarfs are thought to be stars in their last state of evolution. Precisely how the future Sun reaches this area of the H-R diagram (see Figure 5.1) is unknown. The path may be along the sequence of subluminous hot stars, shown in Figure 5.1, since these objects are commonly thought to be very advanced in their evolution.

In the giant and postgiant evolution of the Sun, we have implicitly assumed that the star's mass remains constant. This assumption is probably true for a majority of main-sequence stars, but there is considerable evidence for mass ejection in the red-giant and supergiant stages. This evidence is difficult to handle quantitatively, but it must be understood before giant and postgiant evolution can be discussed with any degree of confidence.

By the time the Sun has reached the white-dwarf stage, it probably will have used up all nuclear energy sources, because the internal temperatures of white dwarfs can support only the burning of hydrogen, which has been exhausted. Further gravitational contraction is impossible because the matter is already completely electron degenerate; in this case, the gravity is balanced by the degenerate-electron pressure (which greatly exceeds the ordinary gas pressure of the nuclei), and for any given mass less than the Chandrasekhar limit there is a unique radius for a totally degenerate star. The kinetic energy of the degenerate electrons is not available, since the electrons are already crowded into all available low-energy states and no further crowding into low-energy states is possible. Thus, we cannot expect any luminosity from the electron-degenerate mass of the white dwarf. The only source available is the total kinetic energy of the nondegenerate nuclei throughout the star. This source of energy is adequate to support a white dwarf with luminosity between 10^{-2} and 10^{-3} $L_\odot$ for about 10^9 years. Thus in a continuously developing region of stars one might expect one star in ten to be a white dwarf; this expectation can be checked for the stars in the neighborhood of the Sun and is found to be approximately true. However, the numbers are somewhat uncertain.

Thus, the Sun as a white dwarf would have a radius of about 10^{-2} $R_\odot$; its luminosity would decrease with a time scale on the order of 10^9 years, with a continual decrease in the internal temperature as the kinetic energy of the nuclei is radiated away. Eventually, it approaches the final state of stellar evolution, a virtually nonluminous mass of degenerate matter, which may be termed a *black dwarf*.

6.3 GENERAL EVOLUTION

In this section, we describe the way in which the evolution is changed for stars with masses significantly different from that of the Sun. For convenience, we treat the evolution of high-mass stars; the Sun is often considered a star of medium mass; but if we arbitrarily define stars of low mass as those whose Schönberg-Chandrasekhar time [Equation (6.6)] is so long that they have not evolved away from the main sequence in the past 10^{10} years, then the Sun is a star of low mass. These stars are either on the main sequence or still in the early stages of evolution toward the main sequence (see clusters, Section 6.4).

This section concludes with a general description of the H-R diagram.

Evolution of Massive Stars

The evolution of massive stars parallels that of the Sun up to the exhaustion of hydrogen in the core and the point of the Schönberg-Chandrasekhar limit. When this limit is reached for the high-mass stars, the contraction of the core begins straightaway; these stars are not partially degenerate in their cores, and hence the higher pressures originating from degeneracy cannot postpone the core contraction and subsequent helium burning, as happens in the low-mass stars.

The contraction of the core is accompanied by a rapidly expanding envelope. The massive stars, then, evolve rapidly to the right in the H-R diagram on tracks which are almost horizontal. Subsequent evolution involves, as before, the onset of helium burning and the return to the vicinity of the main sequence, perhaps through a tendency towards homogeneity. Again, it is thought that these stars eventually become white dwarfs; however, the high-mass stars face an obstacle.

It has been found that stars with masses greater than 1.4 $M_\odot$ cannot become white dwarfs; this is the Chandrasekhar limit. Hence stars of greater mass must undergo some kind of mass ejection (either violent or nonviolent) to reach this thermodynamically desirable state. It has been speculated, for example, that supernovae are the result of massive stars preparing for admittance to the white-dwarf state.

Physically, this limit is traceable to the onset of relativistic degeneracy in the higher-mass stars. To understand this phenomena, we employ crude order-of-magnitude arguments of the same nature as those used in our rough derivation of the mass-luminosity relation in Section 4.4.

Let us assume that the star is in hydrostatic equilibrium and compare the gravitational and pressure forces. The density is given by

$$\rho \propto \frac{M}{R^3} \qquad (6.7)$$

The gravitational force at the surface F_g then goes as

$$F_g \propto \rho \frac{M}{R^2} \propto \frac{M^2}{R^5} \qquad (6.8)$$

We recall that for nonrelativistic degeneracy [Equation (4.15)], the pressure $P \propto \rho^{5/3}$, and hence, from Equation (6.7), we have

$$P \propto \frac{M^{5/3}}{R^5} \qquad (6.9)$$

The force produced by the pressure gradient is then

$$F_p = \frac{dP}{dr} \propto \frac{M^{5/3}}{R^6} \qquad (6.10)$$

For the relativistic case, one begins with Equation (4.16) and obtains

$$F_p \text{ (Rel) } \propto \frac{M^{4/3}}{R^5} \qquad (6.11)$$

When the gravitational and pressure forces are compared for the nonrelativistic case, one finds that these forces depend on a different power of R. Hence, the star can bring itself into hydrostatic equilibrium by adjusting R. This situation does not exist for the relativistic case where the power of R is the same, and we can have a balance of these forces only for some particular value of the masses.

Thus if the mass is too large and the star finds itself in the state of relativistic degeneracy, no equilibrium configuration is possible; the star must lose mass by ejection so that at least the outer parts are not relativistically degenerate. Then, equilibrium can be achieved. This discussion seems to underscore the possible importance of mass ejection for massive stars. If the mass is too small, the star does not encounter the object of the Chandrasekhar limit, and the subsequent evolution goes through the white-dwarf to black-dwarf stage described for the Sun.

The differences in evolution of stars of different chemical composition seem generally to be those required by the observations. For example, the track in the H-R diagram of a star of approximately solar mass but with a reduced abundance of metals lies above the track of a similar-solar-abundance star and has a steeper slope. (See Figure 6.1 and the discussion in Section 6.4.)

The intermediate stages of evolution are not well understood, and no comparison seems profitable. The last or final stages of evolution are probably very similar, since these stages should depend very little on the initial abundance of metals.

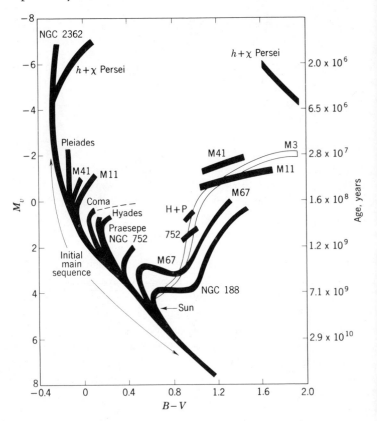

FIGURE 6.1   The composite, cluster H-R diagram as discussed in the text. *After A. R. Sandage.*

The important point in interpreting H-R diagrams in terms of stellar evolution is simply that one does not directly observe any evolutionary star tracks; rather, one observes the locus of the points of a group of stars for a given time—the so-called *isochronical lines*. Occasionally, the tracks and the isochronical lines show a close correspondence; this seems to be the case for the sequence of hot subluminous stars, where the tracks are all rather similar.

Thus, the overwhelming majority of stars are found on or near the main sequence, since the stars spend the largest fraction of their lifetime there. The subsequent evolution away from the main sequence is very rapid; hence, the number of stars observed here is small. This observed fact has been known for years and is called the *Hertzsprung gap;* it is shown in Figures 5.1 and 6.1.

Finally, the fact that massive stars when leaving the main sequence evolve directly to the right in the H-R diagram, while less massive stars evolve up and to the right, leads to a concentration of stars from different parts of the main sequence in the red-giant region. This effect is called *funneling*.

We return in subsequent sections to a discussion of evolutionary effects in the H-R diagrams of specific aggregates, such as clusters.

6.4 CLUSTERS AND EVOLUTION

The properties of a star depend on at least three variables: age, composition, and mass. Galactic and globular clusters may be of great value in the study of stellar evolution, since they appear to allow some separation of the variables involved. For example, the stars in the solar neighborhood are probably heterogeneous in origin; on the other hand, it seems likely that a cluster has stars with a common origin. If these cluster stars have condensed from a common cloud of interstellar material, then we may reasonably assume (at least as a first approximation) that the stars have the same composition and the same age. Thus, the variation on an H-R diagram for a cluster would be due to the stars being of different mass. It is easily seen that great simplification results from these assumptions.

H-R Diagrams of Clusters

It is most illustrative to plot several schematic H-R diagrams for galactic clusters on a composite graph (Figure 6.1). If the distances are not known, the lower main sequences are made coincident to form the diagram. From such a graph, most information can be obtained essentially by inspection.

The various clusters branch off from the main sequence. The curves (except M67) then show a discontinuity, and we find short segments in the red-giant and red-supergiant regions; the Hertzsprung gap is thus clearly shown.

The Hertzsprung gap appears to show a progression, being large for h and χ Persei and nonexistent for M67. It appears that we have a method of ordering the age sequence of the clusters. Clearly, the clusters containing the brighter stars must be very young (recall the discussion of the ages of O and B stars at the beginning of the chapter), and this progression extends down to M67, which must be relatively old (see Table 6.1). These clusters may be dated by noting the point at which the cluster H-R diagram breaks off from the main sequence and by computing the Schönberg-Chadrasekhar time from Equation (6.6). These times are given at the right-hand side of Figure 6.1. Note the very large range in ages.

A check on these ages and some insight into pre-main-sequence evolution can be obtained by studying the H-R diagrams of extremely young clusters. These clusters have an H-R diagram which shows stars above the lower main sequence—stars which apparently are still in the process of gravitational contraction to the main sequence; the fact that large numbers of T Tauri stars occur in these clusters is good supporting evidence for this contention. The problem is to reconcile the age derived from the upper turnoff, for example, NGC 2264, with the presence of the gravitationally contracting stars. Now that the Hyashi stage, namely, a star in convective rather than radiative equilibrium, is recognized as being dominant in the pre-main-sequence contraction stage, the situation is satisfactory; on the older, radiative models, the stars just above the lower main sequence would not have had enough time to reach that position on the H-R diagram in the age of the cluster determined by the turnoff of the upper main sequence and the Schönberg-Chandrasekhar limit. Now the evolution is faster in the Hyashi stage, and the problem is reconciled.

An additional check on these time scales comes from the expansion ages of O associations. The observed proper motions are interpreted in terms of motion at a constant velocity from a common region. This method yields times which are usually a few times 10^6 years.

The schematic H-R diagram for the globular cluster M3 is also shown in Figure 6.1. A comparison of the diagrams for M3 and M67 shows a similar behavior, but the diagram for M3 has a steeper slope as one goes into the giant region. This is in agreement with the theory, as is the general picture implied by the evidence from clusters presented here.

We return to a discussion of cluster H-R diagrams after we introduce the luminosity function.

Evolution and the Luminosity Function

The luminosity function $\phi(M)$ is defined by

$$dN = \phi(M)dM \qquad \text{(6.12)}$$

where dN is the number of stars per cubic parsec with absolute magnitude between M and $M + dM$; often dM is set equal to 1 mag. We would like to see if this luminosity function can be simply related to the birthrate function as a check on our concepts of stellar evolution. The following is assumed: (1) All stars are formed in clusters. (2) The birthrate function is universal throughout the galaxy. (3) The rate of star formation in the solar neighborhood has been constant for the age of the galaxy, taken as 5×10^9 years. This age comes from the oldest galactic clusters, for example, M67, which have been determined from the point at which the cluster H-R diagram turns off from the main sequence and from the Schönberg-Chandrasekhar main-sequence time. The exact value should not be taken too seriously because of uncertainties in the theoretical calculations needed for dating. (4) Stars have an insignificant amount of mass losses. (5) The early main-sequence evolution is adequately described by the Schönberg-Chandrasekhar theory; this implies *no* mixing in the star.

We may then proceed with the main-sequence luminosity function as known for the solar neighborhood. Stars whose Schönberg-Chandrasekhar limit (T_{ms}) is a time *greater* than 5×10^9 years are still on the main sequence, and hence their birthrate is simply the number present divided by 5×10^9 years, or

$$\Psi_{ms} = \frac{\phi_{ms}}{5 \times 10^9} \qquad T_{ms} > 5 \times 10^9 \text{ years} \qquad \textbf{(6.13)}$$

Here the birthrate function Ψ_{ms} has units of births per cubic parsec per year, and ϕ_{ms} is the luminosity function for the main sequence [see Equation (6.12)]. Main-sequence stars whose time T_{ms} is less than 5×10^9 years have all been created within T_{ms}, and hence the birthrate function is just

$$\Psi_{ms} = \frac{\phi_{ms}}{T_{ms}} \qquad T_{ms} < 5 \times 10^9 \text{ years} \qquad \textbf{(6.14)}$$

With these developments, it is a simple matter to begin with ϕ_{ms} (the solar-neighborhood main-sequence luminosity function) and compute the main-sequence birth-rate function Ψ_{ms}; both these functions are shown in Figure 6.2. The birthrate function is rather shallow, showing that the scarcity of early-type stars is due to their fast evolution and not to a deficient birthrate.

These developments can be checked by comparing the birthrate function with the ϕ(cluster) observed in young clusters. As long as we compare stars which have not evolved away from the main sequence, the young-cluster luminosity function should be proportional to the birth-rate function. Indeed, this is found to be the case for clusters where the relevant data are available. To make the comparison in detail, one must allow for evolution on the main sequence and the loss or evaporation of low-mass stars from the cluster. The escape of stars from clusters is caused by tidal perturbations produced by passing interstellar gas clouds. Such

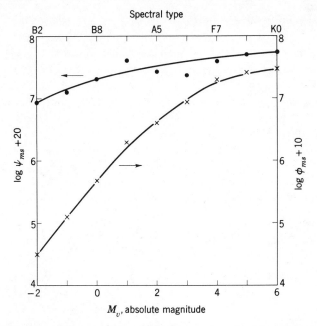

FIGURE 6.2 The birthrate function ψ_{ms} and the main-sequence luminosity function ϕ_{ms} as a function of spectral type and absolute magnitude. Refer to the discussion in the text.

encounters can actually disrupt all but the most dense clusters in, times comparable to the age of the galaxy. These results refer specifically to the *galactic* (i.e., Population I) clusters and deal with the nearly unevolved state of the cluster.

By *unevolved* we mean that the cluster H-R diagram is essentially coincident with the initial or zero-age main sequence, shown in Figure 5.1. We expect that this is the case for clusters which are sufficiently young. Older clusters have evolved away from the zero-age main sequence (as marked in Figure 5.1); the oldest clusters are said to be *highly evolved*, since their H-R diagrams exhibit marked departures from the zero-age main sequence. Any quantity that describes the state or degree of evolution of a cluster or individual star can be termed a *population parameter;* examples are age and the abundance of heavy elements Z.

We now describe how the luminosity function can be applied to highly evolved clusters to determine the semiempirical tracks in the H-R diagram for the galactic cluster M67 and the globular cluster M3. To start, one needs the initial luminosity function (which is proportional to the birthrate function), corrected for the stars which have escaped. Then, the Schönberg-Chandrasekhar theory is used to compute the path of the star up the S-C limit. Refer now to Figure 6.3 for an illustration of the procedure for M67. The basic idea is simply that, once we have corrected the initial or zero-age main sequence for the escape of stars from the

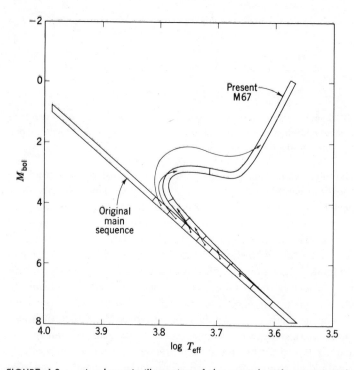

FIGURE 6.3   A schematic illustration of the procedure for mapping the original main sequence (corrected for star escape) into the present sequence for M67, thereby determining the semiempirical evolutionary tracks. Equal numbers of stars are contained in the marked segments on the "original" and "present" sequences.

cluster, all remaining stars are still in the cluster and somewhere on our observed H-R diagram. We do not have to look far for the stars of low luminosity; they are still on the initial main sequence. Stars slightly more luminous than the luminosity at the turnoff point (where the observed H-R diagram turns off from the main sequence) should be only a relatively short distance from the main sequence; more luminous stars should show correspondingly large departures from the main sequence, etc. Thus, we should be able to map by equal number the initial main sequence into the observed H-R diagram and determine the evolutionary tracks.

Consider the first magnitude on the initial main sequence above the turnoff point. Let this interval contain N_1 stars. Now the stars at the bottom of this interval are still essentially on the main sequence. We know that the stars at the top of this interval began on the main sequence, and their present location is given by the distance above the turnoff point on the observed cluster diagram which is required to contain N_1 stars. This procedure is shown schematically in Figure 6.3. Since we know where the star began and where it is now, we have a fairly good idea of its track in the H-R diagram. It is even possible to compute the time required to move across various segments of the path, but this part of the discussion is outside the scope of this monograph.

Considerable information can be obtained from the semiempirical tracks, and in broad outline it is entirely consistent with the present theoretical ideas concerning stellar evolution. In fact, early evolutionary studies leaned strongly on such diagrams. The procedure was to allow the star to evolve in the calculations until its path deviated from the semiempirical track; the calculations would then be stopped and a search begun for the piece of physics being neglected and presumably responsible for the deviation, etc.

6.5 CHEMICAL ABUNDANCES AND NUCLEOGENESIS

The interest in the abundances of the elements stems from two basic areas: (1) they are an important population parameter (see

Section 6.6), and (2) our list of known nuclear reactions should be sufficiently complete for all elements to be produced from hydrogen by nuclear reactions—as is commonly held likely.

Abundance Determinations

The traditional methods for determining chemical abundances in stars have been sketched in Chapter 2. These methods involve the measurement of equivalent widths and the use of the curve of growth. Even the curve-of-growth techniques are only approximate, and considerable effort is required to do a thorough job. Nonetheless, spectroscopic abundances are available for a variety of types of stars; see Figure 2.6 for an example.

Often we are not interested in the abundance of some particular element, but rather in the relative abundance of an entire class of elements. It may be sufficient to know that a star is poor in metals or rich in metals. This can be determined from properly calibrated photometry; for example, the so-called *ultraviolet excess* of F and G stars (reckon with respect to the Hyades main sequence) is an excellent metal-abundance indicator. The ultraviolet excess, namely, the *decrease* in $(U - B)$ over the Hyades value, results from the relative *lack* of blanketing from the absorption lines of the metals; this effect increases the radiation in the U-band pass and hence produces the excess. This method (and others like it) have been calibrated against the spectroscopic results. We return to a discussion of abundances when treating the concept of stellar populations.

Nucleogenesis

Here we briefly explore the abundances of the elements and the possibility of producing all the elements by various nuclear reactions, starting with pure hydrogen. This is a natural question to ask, since the older objects in the galaxy show a tendency to be more nearly pure hydrogen.

The present answer to this question is in the affirmative. Starting with pure hydrogen, there are eight separate types of nuclear reactions required to produce all the elements in stars. These range from the proton-proton chain, the carbon cycle, and the triple-alpha process in normal stars to far more exotic processes in supernova outbursts, etc. A detailed discussion of these problems is outside the scope of this work. Appropriate references are given in the Bibliographical Notes.

6.6 STELLAR POPULATIONS AND GALACTIC EVOLUTION

The concept of stellar populations has been mentioned repeatedly in passing. Now we shall try to make this concept more definite and, specifically, to relate it to the problem of galactic evolution.

The idea of stellar populations was incipient in much data available earlier, but the idea was crystalized in 1944 by W. Baade on the basis of his photographic resolution of the central or nuclear region of M31; this resolution shows (of course) only the very brightest stars, which are red for the central regions of M31 but blue for those found in the spiral arms. Hence, the kinds of stars may be divided into two population types. Population I is characterized by the brightest stars being blue—these are, of course, O and B supergiants. Population II is characterized by the brightest stars being red giants. Once the seed of this idea is planted, the available data on stars can be utilized to further it, and, in fact, Baade published an H-R diagram showing the major differences of the two population types.

The classification of stellar populations can be pushed to include more than two population types. We give here a simple three-type classification, which shows a close correlation with the kinematical properties of the galaxy; the population types take their names from the location in the galaxy. Our simple population types are halo, disk, and arm, and the general scheme is given in Table 6.2; these subsystems are shown schematically in Figure 6.4. Notice that mere location does not determine the population type, since the halo, disk, and arm volumes overlap in space. Kinematical and intrinsic properties are also used.

Most of the typical members in the table are self-explanatory.

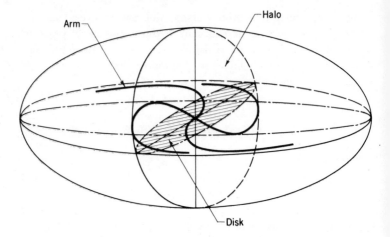

FIGURE 6.4   A schematic, three-dimensional illustration of the three major population types as discussed here; refer to Table 6.1 for additional details.

The various variable stars mentioned are discussed in Chapter 7. The blue subdwarfs are the stars just to the left of the horizontal branch of the typical Population II stars (see Figure 5.1).

The quantity $\langle z \rangle$ is the mean distance from the galactic plane; $\langle v_z \rangle$ is the mean velocity perpendicular to the plane. If the objects discussed are distributed like an ellipsoid of revolution, then c is the semiminor axis and a the semimajor; then, the axial ratio given is a/c. Note also that the ages given are uncertain.

Studying Table 6.2 is tantamount to reading a schematic account of the process of evolution in the galaxy. We may imagine that the galaxy originated as a gravitationally contracting, rotating gas cloud. Star formation and mass loss, where material is ejected from the stars back to the interstellar gas, are thought to have been very rapid in this early stage. The heavy-element abundance of stars increases with time because the hydrogen (and then helium) have been processed in the interiors of stars by nuclear reactions. When some of this material is injected into the interstellar gas, the heavy-element content of the interstellar gas increases. This requires that the ejection go down to the deeper layers, where the nuclear processing has occurred; this implies a cataclysm (such as a supernova) rather than quiet surface ejection. Thus, when a new star is formed from the enriched gas, it begins its existence with a higher initial heavy-element abundance than that of the stars of the preceding generation. For example, the Sun is probably a third-generation star, in the sense that the material has been in three stars before. These "earlier stars" need not be solar-type stars, and are, in fact, most probably very massive stars with very short time scales formed early in the history of the galaxy. Notice that Z (the fraction of heavy elements) increases greatly from the halo to the disk population; hence, it seems likely that star formation and evolution was very rapid during this epoch. If the rate of star formation depends on the amount of gas present, it could well have been more rapid in the earlier stages.

Now the rotation hinders collapse in the plane perpendicular to the rotation axis, but does not hinder it along the axis of rotation. Hence, we have a gas cloud which is constantly flattening; note that the stars formed retain the kinematical properties of the gas cloud at the time of formation. Formation of the disk stars comes

TABLE 6.2   STELLAR POPULATIONS IN THE GALAXY

	HALO	DISK	ARM
Typical members	Globular clusters, RR Lyrae stars (with periods greater than 0.4 day), W Virginis stars, high-velocity stars, blue subdwarfs.	Bright red giants, planetary nebulae, novae, old galactic clusters, weak-line stars, long-period variables (spectrum M5–M9)	Gas, dust, young galactic clusters, supergiants, T Tauri stars, associations, strong-line stars, classical Cepheids
$\langle z \rangle$, parsecs	1,000–2,000	200–500	100–150
$\langle V_z \rangle$, km/sec	~ 75	15–20	~ 10
Axial ratio of subsystem a/c	2	20?	10^2?
Central concentration	Strong	Strong	Little
Distribution	Smooth	Smooth	Patchy
Fraction of heavy elements, Z	~ 0.003	0.01–0.02	0.03–0.04
Age	Old $(5$–6×10^9 years$)$	Intermediate $(1$–5×10^9 years$)$	Young $(< 1 \times 10^9$ years$)$

next; the Sun is a very well-known disk star. This classification follows immediately from the definitions in Table 6.2, the solar age of 4.5×10^9 years, and the observed solar heavy-element content, $Z = 0.015$.

At the present time in the galaxy, star formation occurs mainly in the gas of the spiral arms. The rate of star formation is low at the present epoch; this is not unexpected, since only a small percent of the mass of the galaxy is observed to be in the form of gas; it is conceivable that the amount of gas in the galaxy is higher than a small percent, because dynamical studies indicate that ≈ 50 percent of the mass of the galaxy is in unknown, unobserved objects. These could be gas in the form of molecular hydrogen or very faint stars; the issue is unresolved at present.

This completes our survey of stellar evolution in the galaxy. Much work remains to be done, details verified, etc.; nonetheless, the general outline makes a useful, plausible working hypothesis.

* **7** *   variable
              stars

The variable stars have historically been intriguing and profitable subjects in themselves. However, in this chapter we consider only those variables stars which are important to the discussion of the previous chapters. These are (1) the intrinsic variables, which are important as population indicators and because they occupy restricted regions in the H-R diagram; (2) the cataclysmic variables, which are important in the mass balance and heavy-element enrichment of the interstellar gas; (3) the T Tauri stars, which appear to be newly formed stars; (4) close binary systems, since their evolution may differ significantly from the "simple" evolution applicable to single stars.

Before passing on to these topics, we shall mention briefly a few other types of interesting variables. First, we have the eclipsing binaries. These have been discussed in Chapter 5; they provide an extremely important fund of data on reliable stellar masses and radii.

Secondly, there are the ζ Aurigae systems, which potentially offer the opportunity to study the chromospheres of other stars. These systems generally have a K supergiant primary and a main-sequence B secondary. At times when the B star is eclipsed by the K star, the B star provides an essentially continuous source of radiation, and the atmosphere of the K star can be studied by use of the absorption lines it produces. The portion of the K-star atmosphere that is probed is thought to be the chromosphere. While considerable information is available on such chromospheres, it seems that they are not "normal"; for example, the B star in the ζ Aurigae system controls the ionization in the K-star chromosphere for species with ionization potentials above about 4 $\cdot$ ev. For further details, the reader is referred to the Bibliographical Notes.

Lastly, there are the spectrum variables or spot stars; this topic has been touched upon in Chapter 3.

7.2 THE PULSATING VARIABLES

Here we limit our discussion to the RR Lyrae stars (cluster variables), the classical Cepheids, the W Virginis stars, and the long-period variables. These stars are valuable population indicators because (1) they are all bright (being either giant or supergiant stars) and (2) their period is directly related to their physical properties.

History

Let us consider first the classical Cepheids, which take their name from the prototype star δ Cephei, which was discovered to be variable in 1784 by Goodricke. In 1894, Belopolsky discovered that the radial velocity varied with the same period as did the brightness, namely, with a period of 5 days 9 hr. The variation is such that minimum light essentially coincides with maximum radial velocity, and vice versa. Another well-known Cepheid variable is Polaris.

Such stars are found throughout our galaxy and in other galaxies, including the Magellanic Clouds. The Cepheids in the Small Magellanic were the object of an intensive study by Miss Leavitt, and in 1912 she announced the fact that luminosities of Cepheids were correlated with their periods, in the sense that the longer the period, the greater the luminosity. When Miss Leavitt announced this period-luminosity relation, no Cepheid had a reliable luminosity. The discovery was possible because the stars were in the Small Magellanic Cloud and hence could be considered to be at the same, but unknown, distance. Hence, the relation of absolute magnitude to the log of the period was established without the zero point.

This brings us to the work of H. Shapley. Cepheids were not always thought to be pulsating stars. Indeed, until Shapley's time the prevailing view regarded Cepheids as binaries. The light variations cannot be accounted for in this way (see the Review Questions and Problems). Many weird and wonderful mechanisms, mostly based on some sort of tidal influences, were invoked, but none were satisfactory.

In 1914, Shapley summarized the knowledge concerning Cepheids. He correctly considered them to be giant stars; thus, if one interprets Cepheids as spectroscopic binaries, the mean distance between stars has an average of one-tenth or less of the radii of these stars. Shapley's paper was the deathblow for the binary hypothesis. He argued that the simplest solution to the problem lay in intrinsic variation based on pulsation. Hertzsprung identified the variables in the Small Magellanic Cloud with the similar variables in our own galaxy and began the work of the determination of the zero point; this latter work was actively pursued by Shapley. The zero point has been revised several times, and the values are based on statistical parallaxes (see Section 5.2) for the Cepheids. Some of the confusion in the early work was removed by the recognition of two similar types of Cepheids. The Cepheids belonging to Population I (arm) are called *classical Cepheids* and for the same period are about 1.5 mag brighter than the Population II (halo) Cepheids, which are now called *W Virginis stars* (after the brightest and most completely studied member). Both the classical Cepheids and the W Virginis stars are of spectral type F and G and have a brightness range of about 1 mag.

Period-luminosity Relation—Physical Basis

Let us now discuss the period-luminosity relation and its physical basis; remember that we are discussing stars which are pulsating variables, i.e., *they are not in hydrostatic equilibrium.*

Suppose that the star in question has a region in which the gravitational force exceeds the pressure force by some amount. Then, there will be motion of the material governed by an equation of the form

$$\frac{d^2r}{dt^2} = \text{const} \, \frac{GM(r)}{r^2} \tag{7.1}$$

where the notation is standard [see Equation (4.1)] and where the constant depends on the amount of the imbalance. This equation can be solved for a characteristic time P, which we identify with the period of oscillation, by dimensional analysis closely

related to the approximation techniques utilized in Chapters 4 and
6. Thus, Equation (7.1) becomes

$$\frac{R}{P^2} \propto \frac{M}{R^2} \tag{7.2}$$

where R is the star's radius and M is the total mass. This equation can be rewritten as

$$P \sqrt{M/R^3} \propto P \sqrt{\frac{\langle \rho \rangle}{\langle \rho_0 \rangle}} = Q \qquad \text{(a constant, in days)} \tag{7.3}$$

where $\langle \rho \rangle$ is the mean density and $\langle \rho_0 \rangle$ is a reference density chosen so that Q is in days. This constant Q can be computed from detailed studies of the pulsations; Q is ~ 1 for the stars under discussion here. Thus, the fact that RR Lyrae stars have a period of about 0.5 day (0.3 to 0.9 day), classical Cepheids about 7 days (2 to 40 days), and long-period variables about 250 days (120 to 410 days) is encouraging, since the mean density decreases in the order just mentioned. Note that the periods alone are not sufficient to specify the type of variable, because there are many other types which we do not discuss here; rather, the period, spectrum, range, and form of light and radial velocity variations, etc., are all used in assigning a star to a particular class of variables.

Once Equation (7.3) is established, we are conceptually close to the physical basis of the period-luminosity relation. First, the mass can be eliminated from Equation (7.3) by using the mass-luminosity relation [Equation (4.22)]. Second, an estimate can be made of the effective temperature at mean light and the radius expressed in terms of the luminosity from Equation (1.1). Thus, the period-luminosity is established in terms of supposedly known parameters (Q and T_{eff}).

Basically theoretical discussions are not entirely adequate for establishing the numerical values in the period-luminosity relation; it is better to establish them observationally. Historically (as we have mentioned) in the case of the classical Cepheids, the slope of the period-luminosity relation was established by observations of stars in the Small Magellanic Cloud, i.e., stars at the same distance. The relation was completed by statistical studies of relatively nearby variables.

The RR Lyrae stars occupy an extremely small area of the H-R diagram centered at $B - V = 0.30$ and $M_v = +0.6$. The range in the period of the light variation is small and may well be due to the variation in T_{eff} and R, instead of the luminosity, which is usually taken to be at least roughly constant.

The classical Cepheids have absolute magnitudes between -2 and -7; those with the longer periods are brighter, the brightest having M_v of -6 to -7. The variation in the radius for classical Cepheids (as for most pulsating variables) is some 5 to 10 percent; this is consistent both for the RR Lyrae stars and for the classical Cepheids with a light variation in M_v of approximately 1 mag.

The long-period variables are often called Mira variables after the first such variable discovered (o Ceti); in fact, according to Merrill, it is the first recorded variable star, having been discovered by Fabricius in 1596. This remarkable star has an apparent magnitude varying between 1.7 and 9.6 (!) and a period of 332 days; this period and magnitude range are not atypical for the long-period variables, although the average change in visual magnitude is usually smaller. In addition, the change in bolometric magnitude is probably only about 1 mag; this comes about because of the low temperature of these stars, namely some 2000°K. Thus, a few hundred degrees change in temperature makes a far larger change in the visual magnitude than in the bolometric magnitude. The absolute magnitudes of these stars can be determined by statistical means.

To summarize: the bright and known absolute magnitudes of these objects makes them nearly ideal population indicators. The classical Cepheids are entirely arm population, the RR Lyrae stars are divided into halo and disk population according to period, and the long-period variables are spread throughout the halo and disk population; only the M5 to M9 long-period variables (called the long-period long-period variables) seem to be disk-population indicators.

Finally, we note that these variables occur in restricted areas of the H-R diagram and hence serve as checks on the theory of evolution and stellar structure; eventually these disciplines must explain why and how the variations occur at the particular set of physical conditions observed.

Here we are principally interested in the stars responsible for the injection of nuclear-processed material from stars back into the interstellar medium; obvious candidates are the novae, novalike variables, and supernovae.

A normal nova increases in brightness by a factor of about 5×10^5. Novae before and after the outburst stage are underluminous blue stars with spectra which are relatively featureless. Studies of the ejected material indicate that only 10^{-5} of the mass of the star is lost during one outburst; the outbursts are therefore relatively superficial. The rate of the occurrence of novae (~ 30 per year in our own galaxy) is thought to produce a total mass of ejected material per unit time which is comparable to the contribution from supernovae. Very little is definitely known for the case of the novalike variables.

The supernovae show a brightness increase of a factor of some 10^8, often becoming more luminous than the entire galaxy in which they are found; supernovae in our galaxy are often bright enough to be seen in broad daylight. The Crab nebula (Figure 7.1) is an example of the remnant of a supernova; it is generally taken to have exploded in 1054 A.D. on the basis of Chinese and Japanese chronicles. Only two supernovae have been associated with well-known astronomers; these are Tycho Brahe's supernova (1572) and Kepler's supernova (1604). Approximately a half dozen others are known from ancient chronicles. Detailed discussions of the amount of material contained in this nebular remnant differ, but all agree that a considerable fraction of the star's mass is ejected in the process of a supernova explosion.

The process of calculating the mass of the remnant is too complex to consider here in detail. However, in principle, all relevant mechanisms of emitting radiation must be specified and accounted for. The Crab nebula shows considerable optical polarization and is also known as an intense radio source (around 1 m wavelength) (Taurus A) with a fairly flat spectrum (meaning that the variation with frequency or wavelength is gradual). These facts are satisfied by the hypothesis of synchrotron radiation due to I. S.

Shklovsky. Synchrotron radiation is caused by the spiraling of relativistic electrons around the lines of force of a magnetic field. Rather few electrons are required to give the observed radiation; hence, Shklovsky's realization of the role of synchrotron radiation has considerably reduced the estimated mass of the remnant, compared with earlier estimates.

The rate of appearance of supernovae in our galaxy is approximately one per hundred years. Various estimates show that the amount of material ejected per unit time (at the present rate) is approximately the same order of magnitude for the novae and supernovae. The supernovae may actually be more important for the process of enriching the interstellar medium in heavy elements, because the outburst is far less superficial and because of additional nuclear processes associated with and/or responsible for the supernova outburst.

7.4 T TAURI STARS

These objects are of interest because they are thought to be very young stars which are still in the process of contracting toward the initial main sequence. The T Tauri stars are found embedded in nebulosity—regions of high gas and dust concentration. Besides the connection with nebulosity, T Tauri stars are characterized by irregular light variations with an amplitude of 2 to 3 mag and by a spectrum of type F5 to G5 with emission lines of hydrogen and ionized calcium. The T Tauri stars are clearly associated with the nebulosity in which we find them because their space density within the cloud is approximately one order of magnitude greater than stars in a similar absolute magnitude interval near the Sun.

Measurements of the radial velocities of the various absorption and emission lines indicate that the region of origin of the emission lines is rising, relative to the region from which the absorption lines originate. If we associate the absorption lines with the surface or photosphere of the star and the emission lines with the surrounding envelope, then these two are moving farther apart. Thus, one could easily imagine that the star is, in fact, in the process of formation, in the sense of contraction out of the nebulosity. This idea is reinforced by the appearance of the absorption lines, which suggest that the star is rotating rapidly. Such behavior is thought to be characteristic of young stars which have not had time to shed their excess angular momentum (see Section 6.2).

7.5 BINARIES AND EVOLUTION

Here we briefly touch upon a subject mentioned early in the introductory chapter, that is, most of the stars in the galaxy are binaries (or multiple), and their evolution may be drastically different from the evolution of single stars. At present we can do little more than call attention to the problem.

Consider the problem of the gravitational potential in a reference frame rotating with the stars in a double star system. The potential Ω is composed of the parts due to the gravitational attraction of the stars and a part due to the centrifugal force. We are particularly interested in the two special equipotential surfaces shown schematically in Figure 7.2. Matter in each of the two smaller lobes ($\Omega = \Omega_1$) belongs to the individual star; matter in the region between Ω_1 and Ω_2 is gravitationally bound to the system but not to an individual star; matter outside of Ω_2 has escaped from the entire system.

Now the data available for binaries indicate that main-sequence stars in binaries are similar to main-sequence single stars. How-

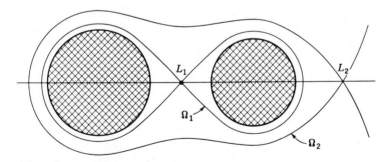

FIGURE 7.2   Schematic surfaces of equal potential in a binary system; see the text for discussion.

ever, this situation cannot persist through the stage in which the star adjusts to the exhaustion of hydrogen from its core and subsequent evolution into the giant region of the H-R diagram. For example, the Sun will increase its radius by orders of magnitude in evolving into the red-giant region. If the equipotential lobe Ω_1 is smaller than the increased radius, a solar-type star in a binary system would have its evolution influenced by mass loss through Ω_1, and its companion could have its evolution altered through the interaction. Thus, the evolution of binary stars which are not sufficiently separated is likely to differ significantly from the evolution of single stars. The many known binaries with gas streams, etc., are strong evidence for this difference in evolution.

The general tone of the text has been optimistic; in view of many past achievements and our present knowledge some of this optimism is justified. However, I hope that the brief mention of the problem of the evolution of binaries will serve as a reminder of the many unsatisfactory aspects of our present knowledge and of the work and discoveries which lie ahead.

BIBLIOGRAPHICAL NOTES

General

The following contemporary elementary texts may be useful:
1. McLaughlin, D. B.: "Introduction to Astronomy," Houghton Mifflin Company, Boston, 1961.
2. Struve, O., B. Lynds, and H. Pillans: "Elementary Astronomy," Oxford University Press, Fair Lawn, N.J., 1959.
3. Abell, G. O.: "Exploration of the Universe," Holt, Rinehart and Winston, Inc., New York, 1964.

The standard text for years, but now, unfortunately, somewhat out of date, is:
4. Russell, H. N., R. S. Dugan, and J. Q. Stewart: "Astronomy I. The Solar System," Ginn and Company, Boston, 1945, and "Astronomy II. Astrophysics and Stellar Astronomy," Ginn and Company, Boston, 1938.

The present text is nicely supplemented by the following monographs (available in paperback):

5. Kiepenheuer, K.: "The Sun," The University of Michigan Press, Ann Arbor, Mich., 1959.

6. Dufay, J.: "Introduction to Astrophysics: The Stars," Dover Publications, Inc., New York, 1964. Here the emphasis is on the observational techniques.

Many useful compilations and references are contained in:

7. Allen, C. W.: "Astrophysical Quantities," Athlone Press, London, 1963.

Chapter 1

Older texts from the turn of the century are:

1. Young, C. A.: "General Astronomy," Ginn and Company, Boston, 1900.

2. Young, C. A.: "Manual of Astronomy," Ginn and Company, Boston, 1902.

3. Clerke, A. M.: "A Popular History of Astronomy during the Nineteenth Century," A. & C. Black, Ltd., London, 1908.

4. Clerke, A. M., A. Fowler, and J. E. Gore: "Astronomy," D. Appleton & Co., Inc., New York, 1898.

5. Moulton, F R: "An Introduction to Astronomy," The Macmillan Company, New York, 1916.

6. Howe, H. A.: "Elements of Descriptive Astronomy," Silver Burdett Company, Morristown, N.J., 1909.

7. Howe, H. A.: "A Study of the Sky," The Chautauqua-Century Press, Meadville, Penn., 1896.

8. Todd, D.: "New Astronomy," American Book Company, New York, 1906.

Historical discussions (on a more advanced level) are found in:

9. Strömgren, B.: On the Development of Astrophysics during the Last Half Century, and The Growth of Our Knowledge of the Physics of the Stars, in J. A. Hynek (ed.), "Astrophysics," McGraw-Hill Book Company, New York, 1951.

10. Struve, O., and V. Zebergs: "Astronomy of the 20th Century," The Macmillan Company, New York, 1962.

This material is reviewed in:

1. Brandt, J. C., and P. W. Hodge: "Solar System Astrophysics," McGraw-Hill Book Company, New York, 1964. See Chapters 4 and 5.

Chapter 3

See Chapter 6 of:

1. Brandt, J. C., and P. W. Hodge: "Solar System Astrophysics," McGraw-Hill Book Company, New York, 1964.

Chapter 4

The basic reference is:

1. Schwarzschild, M.: "Structure and Evolution of the Stars," Princeton University Press, Princeton, N.J., 1958.

The solar interior is covered in:

2. Brandt, J. C., and P. W. Hodge: "Solar System Astrophysics," McGraw-Hill Book Company, New York, 1964.

Chapter 5

See the General References and Chapter 1 of:

1. Schwarzschild, M.: "Structure and Evolution of the Stars," Princeton University Press, Princeton, N.J., 1958.

On a more advanced level, see:

2. Strand, K. Aa. (ed.): "Basic Astronomical Data," University of Chicago Press, Chicago, 1963.

For the interpretation of spectra and the spectral sequence, see:

3. Ambartsumyan, V. A. (ed.): "Theoretical Astrophysics," Pergamon Press, New York, 1958.

4. Aller, L. H.: "Astrophysics, The Atmospheres of the Sun and Stars," 2d ed., The Ronald Press Company, New York, 1963.

Chapter 6

The basic reference for stellar evolution is:

1. Schwarzschild, M.: "Structure and Evolution of the Stars," Princeton University Press, Princeton, N.J., 1958.

A summary from the observational viewpoint is contained in:

2. Sandage, A. R., and L. Gratton: Observational Approach to Stellar Evolution, in L. Gratton (ed.), "Star Evolution," pp. 11–49, Academic Press, Inc., New York, 1963.

The mechanisms required for nucleosynthesis are outlined in:

3. Burbidge, G.: Nuclear Astrophysics, in "Star Evolution," pp. 96–124, Academic Press Inc., New York, 1963.

The concepts of stellar population are thoroughly discussed in:

4. O'Connell, P. J. K. (ed.): "Stellar Populations," Specola Vaticana, Vatican City, 1958.

Chapter 7

Historical information is contained in:

1. Merrill, P. W.: "The Nature of Variable Stars," The Macmillan Company, New York, 1938.

2. Campbell, L., and L. Jacchia: "The Story of Variable Stars," McGraw-Hill Book Company, New York, 1941.

For general information, see:

3. Payne-Gaposchkin, C.: "The Intrinsic Variable Stars," in J. A. Hynek (ed.), "Astrophysics," McGraw-Hill Book Company, New York, 1951.

The properties of the chromosphere of ζ Aurigae are summarized in:

4. Wilson, O. C.: *J. Roy. Astron. Soc. Can.*, vol. 51, pp. 70–74, 1957.

The physics of supernova remnants is thoroughly covered in:

5. Shklovsky, I. S.: "Cosmic Radio Waves," Harvard University Press, Cambridge, Mass., 1960.

Some of the problems of close double stars are described in:

6. Struve, O.: "Stellar Evolution," Princeton University Press, Princeton, N.J., 1950.

Chapter 1

1   Reproduce the numbers given in Section 1.1, supplying details where necessary. (*a*) From Kepler's third law, the known value of the gravitational constant *G*, and the astronomical unit, find the mass of the Sun. (*b*) Given the mean solar angular diameter of 31′ 59″, find the linear value of the solar radius. (*c*) If the solar luminosity is 3.9×10^{33} ergs/sec, compute the effective temperature. How is this value changed because the Sun is not a perfect blackbody?

2   Consult one of the old textbooks given in the Bibliographical Notes (or similar texts) and write a description of the solar atmosphere in your own words based on the text chosen and using the description given by Miss Clerke in Section 1.2 as a guide.

3   Derive the parallax formula used in determining the distances to the nearby stars, marking the appropriate quantities on a figure. What is the distance to a star with a parallax of 0″.1 of arc?

4   Consult an elementary physics text and briefly summarize the experimental evidence (Boyle's law, etc.) which leads to the perfect-gas law.

Chapter 2

1   Carefully describe the difference between absorption and scattering of photons.

2   Define the source function and state its physical significance in terms of the formal solution of the equation of transfer. Describe the physical difference in the source function for a scattering atmosphere and for an atmosphere in local thermodynamic equilibrium.

3   Consult a textbook on elementary differential equations and obtain the formal solution to Equation (2.7). What assumption must be made to reduce this solution to Equation (2.10)?

4   Suppose the Sun were spherical, in local thermodynamic equilibrium, and at constant temperature taken as equal to the effective temperature of 5750°K. Describe how the brightness

of the surface would vary from the center of the disk to the limb.

5 Construct a flow diagram showing the logical steps and physical information necessary for the construction of a photospheric model from observations of solar continuum radiation.

6 Describe (and include a drawing showing) the differences between line formation in local thermodynamic equilibrium and in a selective-scattering–continuous-absorbing medium.

7 Verify that the observational emission gradient β for the chromosphere can be reproduced from Equation (2.21) with $T = 5000°K$, $m = 1.3$ times the mass of the hydrogen atom, and $v_t = 15$ km/sec.

8 A spherical, isothermal atmosphere has a density which follows the formula

$$\frac{N(r)}{N(r_0)} = \exp\left[+ \frac{GM\, m_H\, \mu}{R_\odot\, kT}\left(\frac{1}{r} - \frac{1}{r_0}\right)\right]$$

where r = distance from the center of the Sun in solar radii $R_\odot$
  G = gravitational constant
  M = mass of the Sun
  k = Boltzmann's constant
  T = temperature
  μ = mean molecular weight
  m_H = mass of the hydrogen atom

Use the coronal densities given in the Summary model (Table 2.1) to compute a rough value for the temperature of the corona; assume that it is a pure proton-electron gas.

Chapter 3

1 Make and label a schematic drawing of a sunspot. Summarize the evidence for sunspots being cooler parts of the photosphere and give the physical explanation.

2 Assume that sunspots are at a temperature of 4600°K and have a magnetic field of 1,000 gauss. Compare the magnetic pressure $(B^2/8\pi)$ with the gas pressure; for the material density

in the sunspot, take some typical densities for the undisturbed photosphere from Table 2.1. Should the effects of magnetic pressure be included in the construction of sunspot models?

3 Describe the appearance of facular regions, their relation to sunspots, prominences, and coronal regions, and their time development.

4 Suppose a certain, nearby, solar-type star has a flare of the same area as a solar flare. By what factor must the surface brightness of the flare area exceed the mean, normal surface brightness of this star to produce a 10 percent increase in the total observed radiation? Suppose that the flare on an M-type star (approximately 10^2 smaller luminosity than the Sun) is the same brightness and same relative area as in the previous example. By what factor would the observed brightness of the M star be increased?

Chapter 4

1 From the composition of the initial Sun, namely, $X = 0.744$, $Y = 0.241$, and $Z = 0.015$, compute the mean molecular weight for the solar interior. How has this value changed for the central region of the Sun? Explain.

2 Describe the nuclear processes responsible for energy generation in the Sun. Of what value would the detection of solar neutrinos have in this connection?

3 Describe the physical conditions which lead to degenerate matter. Can a completely degenerate gas cool and emit radiation? Explain.

4 What is the most significant difference *physically* between giants and dwarf stars? Justify your choice.

Chapter 5

1 If star A is ten times brighter than star B, what is the value of $M_A - M_B$ (where the M stands for the absolute magnitude)? What would be the apparent bolometric magnitude of the Sun at a distance of 100 parsecs?

2 Explain the physical origin of the bolometric correction. For which stars is this correction important? [Hint: Consider Wien's

law, which states that the wavelength of maximum emission (per unit wavelength) for a blackbody is related to the temperature by $\lambda_m T = 0.3$ cm-deg.]

3 A certain star (spectral type B) has the following observed quantities: $V = 13.14$, $(B - V) = +0.91$, and $(U - B) = +0.24$. Determine an accurate spectral type, the intrinsic colors, the color excess, and the total absorption. If the absolute magnitude of the star M_v is -2.0, compute the true distance from the Sun.

4 Briefly describe the various direct and indirect methods of determining stellar distances.

5 Briefly describe the spectral changes in stars and their physical origin as one goes from type O to type M.

6 Summarize the basic information which can be obtained through the study of the various types of binary systems.

Chapter 6

1 Sketch the possible mode of the birth of the Sun and its probable evolution. Include a discussion of the possibility of the Sun becoming a supernova at some time in the future. What is the most probable final state of the Sun?

2 Suppose a pure hydrogen star of one solar mass burns constantly at the solar luminosity. How long will its supply of hydrogen last? Repeat the calculation for a hypothetical O-type star of pure hydrogen. Compare these "ages" with the appropriate main-sequence times computed from Equation (6.8).

3 Start with Equation (4.16) and derive Equation (6.13), as indicated in the text. Justify each step.

4 Briefly sketch an account of the evolution of the galaxy. Use the concept of stellar populations as much as possible and summarize the properties of the basic population groups.

5 Show that the motion of the Earth around the Sun satisfies the virial theorem. Identify the internal energy with the kinetic energy of the Earth's orbital motion and identify the resulting relation to complete the demonstration.

1   Of what value are variable stars in the study of galactic struc-
    ture? For stellar interiors?

2   Make a diagram of a binary-star system and show how the
    light and radial velocity vary with phase. Can this behavior be
    reconciled with the observed properties of Cepheids in a
    straightforward way?

3   What role is assigned to supernovae in terms of the evolution
    of stars in the galaxy? Explain how this role could be carried
    by close binary systems.

index

INDEX

Date Due